Love is
a time of enchantment:
in it all days are fair and all fields
green. Youth is blest by it,
old age made benign: the eyes of love see
roses blooming in December,
and sunshine through rain. Verily
is the time of true-love
a time of enchantment—and
Oh! how eager is woman
to be bewitched!

THE SHORES OF LOVE

Sylvia wished that she and Jeremy could have started their life together with nothing harmful behind them. After too short a time together on the ranch in the Canadian rockies, Sylvia's worst fears were realized. Shadows of the past threatened to wreck their marriage that had started so well. Although Sylvia behaved with patience and understanding, disaster loomed continually nearer until she was driven into a dramatic move in a desperate attempt to avert the seemingly inevitable tragedy.

Books by Doris Howe
in the Ulverscroft Large Print Series:

SOME OTHER DOOR
FOREVER MINE
THE SHORES OF LOVE

DORIS HOWE

THE SHORES OF LOVE

Complete and Unabridged

ULVERSCROFT
Leicester

First Large Print Edition
published February 1989

British Library CIP Data

Howe, Doris, *1904–*
    The shores of love.—Large print ed.—
Ulverscroft large print series: romance
I. Title
823'.914[F]

ISBN 0-7089-1944-8

Published by
F. A. Thorpe (Publishing) Ltd.
Anstey, Leicestershire
Set by Rowland Phototypesetting Ltd.
Bury St. Edmunds, Suffolk
Printed and bound in Great Britain by
T. J. Press (Padstow) Ltd., Padstow, Cornwall

FOR

MARY THICKETT

If music be the food of love, play on; . . .
TWELFTH NIGHT.

1

SYLVIA raised herself on one elbow to look through the carriage window. The miles were coming towards her, sliding beneath her, stretching out behind her. She was conscious of space, and time, and distance as never before. She had lost count of the nights when the hours were unbroken by that whirling speed across Canada.

"I never knew about distance before," she mused. She was in a Standard sleeper, comfortable and quiet, with all the bustle outside. She peered around the blind again. How windless and remote and empty the night seemed as it flashed past the window. "Jeremy did this journey less than a year ago. Now he's waiting for me . . ." The thought was warming, dispelling the loneliness. Occasionally she saw the gleam of steel wires and glimpsed the stars speeding across a green sky. She felt the straining of the great locomotive, the pull and grind and roar that was their progress as they hurled forward into the future.

Just what would that future be? This was her last night on the train. Jeremy had arranged to meet her at Kootenay Landing. His ranch lay somewhere along the shore of Kootenay Lake. All the names he had written in his letters had held a romantic ring that intrigued her. Jeremy was English like herself but he had chosen to come here—and now she was joining him. She had wired the probable time of her arrival, and he had said he would watch with great interest as the train travelled across Canada, towards him.

Dear Jeremy, untroubled by any of the nightmares that were still her portion. It must be wonderful to be strong and resolute, knowing where one was going, and what one wanted. Jeremy was equal to meeting whatever life demanded of him, while she felt harassed and uncertain.

She leaned back, feeling as if some of the wind rushing by so silently outside had chilled her warm body. If only she and Jeremy could have started their life together with nothing harmful behind it. She wanted to be to him all that he wished her to be, but there was so much that might hurt them both.

She switched on the bed-light, letting the blind drop. Jeremy was young and demanding, and wanted her to forget all before they met. Yet their meeting was bound in the past; strangely it was from that deep unhappiness that their future together had sprung. She stirred restlessly, wishing the night would pass. Was he keeping vigil, too?

It will be different here, she thought. There will be nothing to remind me. Deborah said that . . . she said I must be strong.

Deborah was Jeremy's stepmother, and Sylvia owed her a debt of gratitude. Her thoughts as she settled down were kinder ones, and she put aside anything of a worrying nature. She was going to Jeremy because she loved him.

The following morning she prepared for the last lap of the tiring journey. She could have flown from Prestwick, across the Atlantic and perhaps picked up another 'plane to the coast, but like Jeremy she had preferred the slower route. She realized now that the time had been restful, and a preparation for her new life, yet a companion would have helped her to keep at bay the increasing introspection of her mood.

Soon after lunch she washed, and changed her suit in the wash-room, feeling that she needed a more attractive outfit than the one she had travelled in. She knew she looked better than a year ago, and hoped that Jeremy would be pleased with the change. Her face held a spirited look, and she was groomed carefully, her dark hair and eyes glowing with new-found health.

At Cranbrook she was so busy making final plans that she did not get out for the usual exercise when the train halted for about twenty minutes. She glanced up at the long travelling coat in the rack above her head, and checked the contents of her handbag. She felt that she was ready when they arrived at Kootenay Landing, which was the next stopping place.

She glanced in her mirror again. Her colour was good and her dark, waving hair shone under the close-fitting hat. Deborah thought she ought to wear brown more often for it suited her brunette colouring;

Sylvia had never cared for black. She looked slim and young in the brown suit. She hoped Jeremy would approve of her.

Someone slid into the seat beside her; most of the passengers were preparing to return to the compartment. Often fellow travellers called to chat with her to help pass the tedium of the journey.

"How far are we from Kootenay Landing?" she asked, half turning.

"I've just come from there . . ." The voice was gay, and she spun round quickly. Jeremy was grinning at her delightedly as he caught her surprise. "Glad to see me, darling?"

She drew a long breath. "Oh, I am . . . but weren't you to wait for me at Kootenay Landing?" She coloured with the surprise.

"I couldn't wait another minute," he told her. "I left home early this morning and came up the line, to travel back with you." He leaned closer until their shoulders touched. The compartment was empty and they seemed to have privacy. "It's been so long, darling." They kissed one another.

"I know Jeremy. I'm here before the

end of April as I promised." She sat erect again as passengers began to fill the compartment, for the train was due to leave. "Oh—am I thankful I tidied up instead of waiting until the last possible moment as I was tempted to do."

Her heartfelt relief made him laugh. "I wouldn't have cared; I know what this journey does to one. Tired of it?"

"Yes. It's been a wonderful experience but I'll be glad to have a night's real rest in a proper bed again."

His eyes were delighting in her, and his face came close, so close that he inhaled the perfume of the powder she wore. He leaned nearer, but she drew back hastily.

"Wait, Jeremy. The other passengers are looking at you in sheer curiosity. They must think I've been keeping you in my suitcase."

His laugh was good to hear. "Who cares? I'll tell them you're my girl . . . I'm going to marry you—how soon, Sylvia?" he added urgently.

When she seemed unable to answer he rose and dragged her by the wrist, through the door of the compartment into the corridor. "I want to talk to you . . ."

For a moment they were quite alone. They felt the train lumber into motion, the sudden alertness throughout the carriages. Jeremy drew her so close to him that she was forced to lean against him to hold her balance. His lips came down on hers in a long, hard, demanding kiss. Sylvia recognized it for what it was, and her soft mouth quivered under the pressure. Her arms went round his waist, and for several moments they lost count of their surroundings.

"I'm terribly in love with you—did you know?" he whispered unsteadily. "Letters are most unsatisfactory . . . this is much better. Do you know—you're away prettier than I remembered too. Oh, darling, I love you . . ." His arms tightened and he kissed her again and again in deep emotion. He still held her in that close embrace.

"Oh, Jeremy—let me go . . ." she whispered, colouring with shyness.

He laughed against her face. "I couldn't bear that strangeness between us. You were shy, weren't you? For heaven's sake don't be shy with me, Sylvia. We're too close for that."

"Let me go. Someone is coming." They stood apart, and she tried to tidy her hair. Jeremy bent and kissed it, one arm round her waist possessively.

"You don't really mind?" he asked in a low tone.

"Jeremy—you're sweet. I just can't take it all in somehow. Let's return to the coach now, dear—please."

She picked up her brown shoulder bag which had slipped out of place, and settled it on her shoulder. He touched it restlessly.

"That's a good idea for long distance travelling." He followed her back to the compartment and they settled in their seats. She pushed her hand under his arm and he gripped her fingers. "That's better. You're glad to see me, aren't you?"

"You know I am. Glad in so many ways, too. Jeremy—I've brought just about everything I own." She looked into his eyes questioningly.

"That suits me just fine," he assured her in so hearty a manner that they both laughed again, in spite of their emotion.

Nervousness caused her to break into impetuous speech. "I've brought back the money you sent for my ticket; I didn't need it. I sold the furniture of the flat and —I didn't tell you before, but Morgan left me something. It was such a surprise. I had to accept it although I didn't want to at first, but . . . well, it was over four thousand pounds." She felt in her bag for the envelope which she had checked several times on the journey. Being able to return the money to him spelled her own independence. It was not his money that was bringing her out to him. She was coming of her own accord and had freedom of action now.

He took the envelope without comment, and put it in his pocket. She felt his displeasure and knew she had spoiled their meeting. "I wish you'd used it . . ."

She saw that he was disappointed. "I thought you might be pleased that I had come because I wanted to come—not because your money was bringing me."

"Ah! I hadn't thought of it like that." His face cleared instantly of the doubt. "Look, darling, we can be married in Nelson on Monday. Will that be all right for you? I've got the licence and we can be married any day you want. Monday is the earliest so I naturally got Monday fixed in my mind."

She evaded the question by asking: "Where am I going until then?"

"I've booked accommodation for you in Locker—that's about two miles from the ranch, which is your future home, in case you've forgotten. I shall call to see you every day until you decide, so you won't be lonely. Your room is ready for you—Mrs. Dell showed it to me yesterday."

"I'll certainly be glad to get into it," she said. "Thank you, Jeremy."

"I'm looking forward to showing you round my ranch but that can wait until tomorrow." He glanced at his watch. "We'll arrive in about ten minutes. Is this the only case you have in here with you?"

"Yes, I'd just closed it when you came. My coat is on the rack."

He lifted it down, and helped her into it. Others were preparing to vacate the train, and under cover of the bustle, he embraced her again. Sylvia realized the surge of emotion between them, and knew he was delighted to be with her after the long separation.

He was looking at her curiously, critically, so close that she could not evade him. "I never realized before what sad eyes you have, darling. They are lovely— lustrous and so dark—but infinitely sad." He spoke slowly, as if making a discovery.

She moved away restlessly. She was afraid that her eyes might betray her, and she smiled brilliantly to appease him.

There was not time for more conversation for the train was running in to the Landing, where a boat was waiting to take some of the passengers further up the lake. Sylvia followed Jeremy from the coach, speaking to acquaintances, as they all prepared to embark. They had come across a continent together and would probably never see each other again, yet each had served a purpose, or filled a niche.

She stood quietly waiting while Jeremy went to look for her trunks. How handsome he looked as he moved assuredly among the crowd. He was tall, and broad shouldered. His golden head shone in the late sunshine, his face was brown from the outdoor life he now lived. He looked alert and full of vigour to his finger tips.

She shivered in the heat of the

afternoon, knowing that Jeremy would be her husband. She was unable to realize it to the full even now, but she held to one thought with determination. Jeremy loved her. There could be no doubting that. He came towards her.

"Ready, darling? I've got the trunks on the car. We have quite a distance to go yet."

Several people claimed her attention, and he waited patiently as she bid them good-bye. She finally took his arm and they walked towards the car. Over all the bustle of arrival there was a silence, and an atmosphere she could sense. Against the enclosing mountains there was a depth of peace which their trivialities could not reach.

"This is easy," she told him gaily. "I know what happens now. We follow the lake road until we come to Locker, then we stop and you push me out, and you continue on to the ranch alone." They had been over it so many times in their letters.

"How long will I be alone?" he asked her bluntly.

"Not long, Jeremy."

It was the first time she had not evaded

the issue, and he was pleased. Her reluctance had not escaped him. She got into the car, and he slid into his place at the wheel. They were off, leaving a small crowd behind them at the Landing. Sylvia knew that Jeremy had been impatient until they could be alone.

"I can drive with one hand," he suggested presently.

She edged away in pretended horror. "Not while we are so close to the lake. Oh, you never told me it was like this. It's so huge! Why, anything could happen on this mountain road. Do you ever have landslides? Does anyone fall in? What is it like here on a dark night? I feel quite overpowered."

Her voice was so genuinely impressed, and her gaze so far-distant that he laughed in amusement. The mountains towered above them on both sides of the lake, tree-clad and richly green.

"All right—I can wait. Surely I told you the lake was big? Anyway, what's it matter right now? Let us talk about us instead. Are you glad to be here?"

"Yes, I feel very happy. Can't think why either."

"Could it be my presence?" he suggested softly.

"Could be."

"Do you know something, Sylvia? You've one of the most charming speaking voices I have ever heard. I'd forgotten it was so enchanting. It's why those people wanted to talk to you just now at the Landing; they just wanted to hear your voice. I'm lucky to be in a position where I can hear it often."

"Thank you, sir." She smiled at him thoughtfully. She was exhilarated for he was so attractive, attentive, and pleasant. All would be well if she held her peace. On Monday they would be married. "Which way is Nelson?" She followed the sequence in her mind.

"Back there . . . why?"

"Far?"

"Not as distances go out here. Why?"

"What a man for questioning me," she complained. "I never heard of Nelson before half an hour ago and you expect me to know all about the place."

"I see." He swerved close under the mountain that towered above them, and stopped the car. "I told you we were going

14

to be married in Nelson, didn't I? You were thinking of that. Well, I'm thinking of it too. Oh, Sylvia . . ." His fair head came close to hers, and his arms went round her, holding her close. "This is our first moment without a crowd around. Tell me that you care too. I can't bear it if that isn't right between us. I love you so dearly. Tell me . . ." He waited in sudden stillness.

She could not have answered him half an hour ago but now she was steadier. "Yes, I care, Jeremy. I've cared for a long time. The circumstances are against us but don't be so anxious, darling. Give me time to readjust. We don't know each other very well . . ."

His face moved against hers restlessly. "You're so gentle and sweet and I love you. If I get you I gain everything that is worth while in the world."

"Yet what do you know of me?" She questioned in a troubled way.

"I know more about you than you guess. I've had my eye on you a long time. Longer than you know. But we're not going to be serious today, darling. You're here and the magic's started . . ." She tried to respond to his mounting ardour, tried to reassure him and herself that all was well between them.

After a while he began to question her about his stepmother and brother whom she had seen recently in England. He was content to sit with her in his arms as she tried to give him a picture of their lives since he left home.

"Deborah was so good to me, darling. I can't tell you of their kindnesses to me. It was partly for your sake—but some of it was for mine, too."

He laughed against her. "Amazing . . . no wonder they liked you. I do. Do you like me, darling?"

"Yes." She put both hands to his face and kissed him soundly. "There . . ."

He flushed, and sat erect, brushing both hands through his fair hair. "You're a honey—and I'm a brute, keeping you here like this when you must be tired. We'll soon be in Locker now, where you can relax, darling. One more kiss, my love, to keep me going."

He started the car and drove on towards a small wooden house she noticed by the lake-side. Jeremy carried in her suitcase, and she followed slowly along the path, feeling the quietness, now that the engine had stopped running. There was a hum of bees from somewhere behind the building, but the gentle, insistent sound intensified the stillness. A woman came to greet them, smiling through the screen door before she opened it to them.

"You're welcome, Jeremy. Is this your girl?" she asked heartily.

Jeremy introduced them. Sylvia liked her hostess, for her appearance was clean and matronly and comfortable. After the noise of the past two weeks it felt strange to be static and quiet again. It was like plunging into cold water after a steam bath.

"I live here alone," Mrs. Dell said. "Yes, it's always quiet, but I like it that way. Once in my life I had all the noise I wanted—it's better like this." She led the way to the room Sylvia would occupy. "Will you be all right here?"

"I certainly will. How nice it is. It's so restful and fresh and . . ."

"You're tired, aren't you?" Mrs. Dell summed up the situation astutely. "I know what that journey is. I'll get a meal right

17

away." She left them, and Jeremy placed the case he carried in one corner of the room.

"I'll take the trunks forward to my place," he said casually. "Nothing in them you'll want for a few days, is there?"

She smiled, knowing he wanted the assurance of having something of hers at his ranch, because she would follow her belongings. "I won't need them . . ."

She slipped out of the heavy coat and put it on the bed. Her brown suit had a gold and black fob hanging on the lapel, and she straightened it nervously as she turned back to him. Jeremy held out his arms and she went to him.

"I'm going now, Sylvia—but I'm coming back tomorrow—and every to-morrow until . . ." He kissed her on the lips and she knew that she could not play with Jeremy. She had come out to marry him and must do just that. He looked meaningly into her eyes, holding her gaze deliberately, before he walked to the door. He smiled tenderly at her and quit the room.

Sylvia sank into a chair, surprised that her legs were trembling. She stayed there thinking deeply until Mrs. Dell called to her that supper was waiting. The meal was a quiet one, broken only by their desultory conversation. She learned something of the district, and a lot about her hostess who enjoyed such a patient listener. She was glad when she could escape to her room.

She stood for a while in front of her window, watching the gleam of the lake that could be seen between the frame of the trees. She felt the romantic atmosphere, the difference from anything before experienced by her.

After London this is going to seem like heaven on earth, she mused. I wonder how long one feels the rolling motion of the train? This must be how a sailor feels for a while on shore.

Presently she fell asleep to the subdued, distant sound of the lake water pushing against the stony beach.

The nightmare returned in the defencelessness of exhausted sleep. She tried to evade that relentless, pursuing voice, that was for ever dragging the confession from her shrinking soul. Only half asleep she tried to struggle against those dreams that were deeper than dreams, before they submerged her in agonizing fear.

Tell me what really happened?

She heard herself say: *We didn't really quarrel—but he came in drunk and was very sick. It was only like many other evenings. I covered him on the couch . . .*

Yes—and what then? The voice prodded her relentlessly.

She remembered that Morgan's gaze had been resentful. Had he known her intention? *I was afraid of him. I ran to the door —he followed me, lurching a bit—I don't know what he intended to do. I felt his hands on me, drawing me back through the doorway. Then—I must have slipped on the carpet at the head of the stairs— he tried to save us both, but we overbalanced . . .* She shuddered in the dream, seeing again the terrible crash that had resulted in Morgan's death. *I was underneath—I thought I'd taken most of it, but he knocked his head . . .* She covered her face with both hands, and tried to struggle out of the nightmare.

You knew a fall might be fatal—you knew about the plate in his head . . . The words drowned her again. *You meant to leave him, didn't you? After four years of marriage you were walking out on him. You didn't love him . . .*

It was torture to have their relationship defined by Morgan's mother. *I blame you for his death, Sylvia.*

It was an accident. It was. It was. We fell down the stairs. Oh, it needn't have happened; if only he hadn't followed me.

You acted like a frightened schoolgirl. He tried to save you both; you said that.

Sylvia had felt his surge of strength as he tried to save them both from disaster. *Yes—oh, please don't say any more. We are hurting each other unbearably . . .*

There will be an inquest, and I'll see you through it—but this you must know . . . as long as I live I'll hold you morally responsible for the death of my son. Whatever the coroner says, whatever his verdict, you and I will know the truth.

No—take that back, Sylvia whispered. *You must, or I can't live . . .*

You'll live, and you'll forget; it is I who will never forget.

It was her gentleness and youth that Morgan had wanted, yet he had not guarded either quality. His voice came to

21

her coldly, loudly, piercing through the uneasy clouds of sleep.

I'll murder you before I'll let you walk out on me . . . you'll never get away. Never. His face, distorted with dark passion made her whimper with sudden pain. She had been flying from him, from his cruelty when the accident happened. It *was* an accident, she whispered in her dream; if only I could be sure . . . sure . . . had he meant it to be more than that? And in the final moment realized, and tried to save us both? If I knew . . .

Jeremy Lang drifted into her dream, and she smiled; he had called round to help as soon as he heard. He had been white-faced, taut. *I read it in the papers. Can I help?*

The inquest was not quite the evil thing she imagined it might be. There was none of the naked suspicion that Morgan's mother had felt. It was all clear, save in Sylvia's mind. How could she ever be sure now that Morgan had intended to kill her? She sighed. When she returned to the flat she rang Jeremy. *Can you come over? I'm going crazy.*

They walked in Hyde Park together. It

was a mild spring day. About their feet were yellow, purple and orange crocus. The grass was studded with them. She was out of tune with the freshness of the spring day, but roused herself to talk to Jeremy.

I was going to leave him, she whispered. *That's why it hurts so much. Weeks ago it was all finished between us. I'm to blame for everything—he was so angry.* She glanced up into the cloudless sky. *It must be awful to die in the springtime.*

Why blame yourself so bitterly? It was an accident. You heard the verdict . . .

She knew then that she would never be able to tell anyone of that final bitter quarrel. Soon after that Jeremy took her to his stepmother. He was planning then to come to Canada and he wanted her to follow him when she was strong again. She shivered, remembering those weeks of stark despair.

I loved you before Morgan died, but I would never have spoken. I'm pushed for time or I'd have taken this slower. Promise you'll follow me. You must wear my ring . . .

I can never forget—what has been, she whispered.

You must try. I'll make you forget, darling. I want you so much. You will be my wife one day, when this sadness is finished with. Won't you—won't you?

Yes, I want to be, Jeremy.

When you join me I shall be the happiest man in the world.

She wakened from the dream, pulling out of it as if from delirium. Dream and reality were now one, for she was here in Canada, and tomorrow Jeremy would be with her again. The past was finished, he demanded the future. She trembled as she lay thinking, trying to subdue her agitation. If only the past might be wiped clean as a slate is wiped with a duster.

The following morning she had not finished breakfast when Jeremy appeared, striding eagerly down the path from his car.

"Good morning, darling. Feeling rested this morning?"

"Yes—and I'm late." Her soft brown eyes rested on him gently. "Can you wait until I finish this coffee? Mrs. Dell makes it like no one else and I can't bear to leave any of it."

"I'll have a cup with you." Jeremy poured himself a cup from the percolator. As he sat down he ran his hand quickly over her dark, shining hair. "Feel like facing life again?"

"Yes."

"Good," he spoke softly. "We've a lot to settle today."

She went to fetch her coat, and presently Mrs. Dell followed them to the door to see them off. Jeremy opened the car door for her and she got in. He stepped over her knees to the driving seat.

"Yes, I *could* have gone round, but I didn't." He started the car and she waved to Mrs. Dell, before turning her attention to the scenery. Most of the houses stood high above the road, commanding magnificent views of the lake and shore for miles. The approach to them was often up small and very steep lanes. Sylvia scarcely knew what to expect when she thought of Jeremy's home, although he had discussed his property at some length in almost every letter. When they drew into a small lane, she turned her eyes to question him.

"Yes, this is it, darling. It's bigger than some of the fruit ranches around here and

25

stands further back. Like it? You're awfully welcome . . ."

The wooden cabin was surrounded by trees, and backed by the mountain on which it appeared to grow. No other property appeared to lead from this lane and she loved the privacy this offered.

"It's charming—and typically Canadian." She was so responsive that Jeremy smiled. She had a feeling that whatever she said would be satisfactory, for he liked it so well himself. "It's far, far ahead of any other ranch in the district. Like something out of a fairy story. Honestly, it's so much nicer than I had dared to hope."

He was grinning, his hands playing with the gears as they sat looking. "When I first arrived I thought I was having an hallucination. There was smoke going up from the chimney, yet no one could have known I was coming. Well, I dumped my bags, opened the gate and strolled up to the cabin. The door was opened by an old chap called Dan. He looked—distinctly peeved when I said who I was. That's an understatement, by the way. I gathered that he had been living on the place for a couple of years, telling people in Locker that he was my uncle."

She looked at him in amazement. "What a nerve . . ."

"Sure. But he put on such a decent meal that we got talking. He said he wanted to stay—would have stayed indefinitely if I hadn't shown up. I turned him out of my room but hadn't the heart to turn him off the place. He sleeps in a lean-to at the back, does all the cooking and helps in the garden. Owing to his care of the place it was all in fairly good condition. I haven't mentioned him before because I wasn't sure whether you'd want him around."

"Oh, Jeremy, I don't care. It's all completely lovely. What an enchanting garden. There is so much colour—and the trees make a wonderful background."

"Let's get into the house and look round." When they approached the door a dog bounded forth, looking as if he meant to eat someone. "Bing—get down —this is someone very special—and not for eating." He did not raise his voice and the animal subsided obediently.

"I like dogs," Sylvia said. "I think I like you . . ."

Bing allowed her to stroke his brown and black coat until an old man came out to investigate the noise. He had evidently been washing windows for he still held a leather in gnarled hands. Jeremy introduced them.

"I'm very glad to meet you," Sylvia murmured.

"Are you, miss?" Dan looked taken aback.

"Oh, yes. Any—uncle of Jeremy's is an uncle of mine."

Dan chuckled noisily, and shook her hand with good will. Bing capered round them as they went indoors. Sylvia thought the cabin was cleaner and more comfortless than the proverbial new pin. Everything that could be made for relaxation in living had been carefully hidden. There was the bare furnishing and nothing more.

"Something missing," Jeremy spoke uneasily. "We can't think what it is either."

"Curtains," Sylvia supplied promptly. "Cushions—books—a pair of slippers—some knitting—your tobacco tins—boots —the dog dish—you have tidied up to some purpose. I shouldn't think you'd ever be able to find anything again as long as you both live." She stood laughing at them, amused and touched.

Jeremy knew himself discovered. "We've been at it since daylight . . ."

Dan relaxed visibly and followed them into each room in a proprietary manner that amused Sylvia. Everything was clean and bare and without comfort.

"Practically a bungalow," Dan told her. "Except for that lower room. I tried to persuade Jeremy to have it floored and made into a garage but he wouldn't."

"I wanted to know what you thought first," Jeremy said. They both talked to her and at her, ignoring each other in a way that was intriguing. "You might have ideas for that lower room. It doesn't have to be a garage when we have so many sheds about."

She peeped into the room in question, surprised by its size. "I can't really see everything in the first quick look. Oh, it's all charming."

They returned to the main room, where she saw that the outer door was seldom shut save to keep out the weather. Dan had several dishes cooking and the odour was good. When she and Jeremy returned from a quick look outside, he had the midday meal set on the long table.

"We don't have to keep Dan," Jeremy said teasingly. "I like him and he wants to stay, but if you don't want a stranger around then he can go."

Sylvia looked up at Dan, wondering how he would take this. Something in the old man's gaze hurried her into speech. "Please don't change anything. I hope he'll stay. I like him, too."

Dan relaxed, and returned to his cooking. He grew loquacious and highly coloured under her praise.

"I learned my cooking the hard way—I used to live up north, panning for gold, and we got into some queer corners sometimes. I've cooked in the ground, in an old tin, and in mud, and I learned to put the taste in things in them days."

Sylvia helped him to wash up after they had eaten, while Jeremy waited impatiently. "Oh, come on, Sylvia . . ." He took her to the slope overlooking the lake, with an uninterrupted view up and down the great waterway. The colouring was exquisite, ranging from the more sombre greens to mauve and purple where the mountains appeared to be smudged by some giant artist.

"Jeremy . . ." she spoke solemnly. "Is it that you have no appreciation of beauty —or just that it did not occur to you to tell me?"

He grinned at her. "I thought I'd let you discover it for yourself. This is the place that's been putting up with me for the past year."

"Rather nicely phrased. It's utterly breathtaking. How long have you owned the ranch?"

"Years—my father helped me to buy it originally, then I had a spell in England and now I'm back for good. You like your new home then, darling?"

They were out of sight of the cabin, and she knew he had drawn her away deliberately. She drew a sharp breath. It was here at last and she did not know how to meet it. "Oh, Jeremy . . ."

"Still not quite sure about me?" It was like him to utter a direct question.

"I was—when I left England . . ."

"And now?"

"I lost all my assurance on the way."

31

She felt his impatience. "You'd not just say that to keep me guessing?"

"I would not. I'm upset, too. It's just one of those things." She knew that her words were like a dash of cold water on his enthusiasm, and she was bewildered by her own indecision.

"Do you want to talk about it?" he demanded.

"I don't want to hurt you."

"No one is going to get hurt," he told her grimly. "You're just about the nicest thing that ever happened to me, and I'm not taking any risks. There is one small matter that you appear to have overlooked, however—that is that we're still engaged. You accepted my ring—that still stands for something and I'm not letting you forget it either."

"I do not forget."

"You know what I think is the matter —you've had too much time on your hands on the trip out and have scared yourself—that's all it is." He regarded her speculatively, his eyes narrowed against the glare of the sun.

"Could be. Sometimes I feel as if I don't really want to marry again. The first time hurt me too much." She could not meet his look, and turned her head away.

"You'll soon lose that feeling when we're married."

"*If* we are married . . ."

"*When* we are married, because I hold you to our bargain. This indecision will pass. Come on, let's go further down the slope and sit down." He put out his hand to help her, and she followed him. The breeze was fresh and brisk, but when they sat down they could not feel it. The sun was high, but not strong enough to burn them. Sylvia enjoyed the feeling that being in the open air always gave her. If her mind had been at ease she would have enjoyed an afternoon sitting out there on the hillside. But Jeremy had brought her here for a purpose, for privacy, while they threshed out the points of their joint future welfare. She leaned on one elbow while he sprawled full length near her.

"Now—let's have it." His tone had changed, become harder. "We are agreed more or less on one point . . . that you can't back out of your engagement."

"What would you do if I did?" she considered him gravely.

"Sue you for breach of promise." They both laughed, for the idea was absurd. "But it's not coming to that—you don't want it to, do you?"

"No," she agreed. She knew that he was determined, and he was a harder man to cross than she had imagined. He had made up his mind irrevocably, and nothing during the past few months had shaken his resolve. The waiting had but stiffened that resolve. There was no help to be gained from his grim expression, and she gazed down at the dry grass she was twisting nervously between her fingers.

Jeremy rolled over until he was close to her. His hand arrested her nervous fingers. "You're not scared of me, are you?"

She shook her head at the question. He looked very handsome today, completely male, carefully shaved, and wearing a leather sports coat and brown corduroy trousers.

"Well, that's something. Don't let's fight each other. Just relax. I want to tell you what you mean to me. These past months have shown me, if I didn't know before. I believe we were meant for each other. You just met Morgan first and married the wrong man. I was coming along if you'd waited."

She looked away from him again. "Yet we should not have met, save through him . . ."

"Who's to know that for sure? What is done can't be undone. I love you and I think you care more for me than you know at the moment. You're very nice to me, anyway. Given half a chance we can be happy together." His argument was persuasive and she saw that he believed it. His arms came close about her. "Weren't you glad to see me when I met you on the train. Didn't it mean anything to you?"

She laughed shakily. "You know it did. I was thrilled and flattered, to have a handsome man come all that way to meet me. I loved it."

"So you think I'm handsome?" He buried his face against her.

"Yes. But it's the last time I shall tell you so; I don't want a vain man on my hands." She spoke energetically.

"Then you're sticking to your bargain?" he asked quietly.

"You're not letting me do otherwise, are you?"

He glanced up into her face. Deliberately he moved to kiss her, and she tried to respond. He felt the gentleness of her soft mouth and took fire from it, so that the kiss lengthened. Sylvia tried to end it, and wrenched her face away. He held her a moment longer.

"You were frightened . . ."

"Well, really, Jeremy . . ." her voice shook.

"You were frightened because you don't love me. A woman in love doesn't fear."

"Was it that? You'd better let me go," she spoke stiffly.

"No. We'll be married on Monday . . ." She felt his returning coldness, and knew he had not relished the rebuff. When she had been willing to come six thousand miles, he could not understand her reluctance now.

"Oh, I'm acting foolishly. Put it out of your mind, Jeremy . . . will you, please?"

"I will because it has just occurred to me that you don't know the meaning of love."

"Yet I've so much painful living behind me. I'm nearly twenty-five—a widow—I should know all the answers—does that sound callous? I don't seem to know much about anything, do I?"

He laughed in spite of his anger. "We've both plenty to learn. Don't worry if you can help it, Sylvia. Let's take what comes, eh?"

She sighed, knowing he was trying to help her. "I think I'd better go now. Do you mind? I can walk . . ."

"No, I'll drive you down."

Dan and the dog were nowhere to be seen as they left the ranch a few minutes later. Jeremy's face was hard; his expression defied analysis. Sylvia knew she had antagonized him. Even now she had the power to change his mood if she cared to try, for his love gave him understanding. Instead, she sat silently by his side as they bowled along the road towards Mrs. Dell's house. When they reached the ranch Sylvia got out of the car and closed the door after her.

"I'm sorry, Jeremy."

He nodded coolly. "I know. Tomorrow is Sunday—care to come swimming with me? I'd call for you after lunch."

This was something that would please him and she agreed. "I'd like that."

"I'll come about two o'clock." He touched his hair in a salute, glanced at her briefly as she turned away. He backed, for the road was narrow, and was soon out of sight.

"I wish . . ." she shaded her eyes as she watched the car disappear.

The following morning she helped her hostess about the house, and the hours flew. When Jeremy arrived she greeted him cheerfully, feeling more composed. She wore a cotton washing frock over her swimsuit, and had rubber shoes on her feet. Jeremy made no effort to kiss her as they left the house together and walked down the shingle.

The water was calm but intensely cold. The lake was fed from the snows that melted on the mountains, and she knew its size accounted for the chill. She shivered and Jeremy smiled for the first time.

"A bit of an effort. Give me your hand and I'll help you in." His voice was more cordial than it had been so far today.

She slipped out of the cotton frock and was ready. "Am I a coward?"

"No." His narrowed eyes took in the

neat figure and dainty limbs. "You're pretty—did you know?"

She stood near him, tucking in a stray hair under her rubber cap. "Don't swim out too far, will you?"

"No. I'll take care of you." He plunged in, and she followed, gasping as the chill water shocked her warm body.

"Brrr!" After the first paralysing moment the feeling lifted, and she experienced a buoyancy that was good and energizing. She followed him into deeper water, for she was an excellent swimmer.

"I come down here nearly every day," he shouted. "I've not been in for nearly two years." For half an hour they swam and floated, enjoying the exercise, talking spasmodically, until Sylvia began to tire. "I've had enough. I'm going in."

"All right. I'll swim out a bit and then join you." He struck out powerfully for the centre of the lake, while she turned back to the house to dress. She was only away from the beach about five minutes, yet on her return there was no sign of Jeremy. She gazed carefully across the gleaming water, not seeing him. Surely had he been out there, there should have been some ripple, some sign of his fair head, some flashing of arms? The thought of danger brought sudden terror and panic. She ran wildly along the shingle, calling his name.

If Jeremy died out there . . . a large bird hovered close to the surface, seeking something. She kicked off her shoes, and slipped the dress down from her shoulders. Premonition drove her on and she was running wildly towards the water when Jeremy's voice hailed her from the trees. She spun round as if he had shot her. There was no chance to compose her features.

"Sylvia—what on earth are you doing?" Jeremy hurried towards her.

She cast herself into his arms. "Oh, I thought you were still out there— drowning." Her hands clutched his shoulders nervously as if to reassure herself.

"Were you going in?"

"Yes—to find you. Look—that bird. I thought he could see you under the water. I thought you might have got cramp." Her eyes were still anguished.

"He's only hunting for his supper. Why

didn't you give me a shout? I was keeping out of sight until I was dressed again."

"I never thought of that. Oh, it's given me such a headache."

"Better put your dress on again, darling, or someone might come along and wonder." He bent on one knee and untied the shoe she had kicked off hastily a few minutes before. He felt how she trembled and was surprised. "Push your foot into this."

He untied the second one and helped her on with that, too. When he stood up again he drew her along the beach to a more secluded part where they would be free from possible observation. They sat down side by side and looked at one another. Jeremy threw back his head and laughed aloud.

"You dear little fool—you do care about me."

"I know. Just for a minute I knew that life would be ended for me if you were out there under the water. It was a blinding flash of truth. I wouldn't have wanted to live—isn't it a terrible thought?"

"Not to me. That's the way it is with me, too. I'm glad we've found out before

41

tomorrow. No man wants a reluctant wife —certainly I didn't. Now it's different." He bent to look into her downcast face. "What would you have done if I had been out there?"

"I wouldn't have come back without you," her eyes filled with tears of reproach.

"Thank you, darling mine." They sat hand in hand. "May I?"

There was no hesitation about her this time. She made haste to comply, and the kiss they shared was the first genuine response of passion he had had from her.

"That's better. I'm glad this has happened, although you've been so frightened. I couldn't have managed it half so well if I'd deliberately planned it. You do care . . ."

"Yes. I love you, Jeremy. The roots were deeper than I knew. I must just have been thinking too much on the journey as you said, and scared myself."

Her words filled him with content. "My luck must have changed."

"I hope nothing happens to us for the next twenty years," she said passionately.

42

"I hope fate forgets about us so that we can grow into nice sound vegetables."

"Would that content you?" he asked her, smiling at her expression.

"I think it would—for a long time. I've been so hurt that it feels as if the scars must be visible on me. Are they?" She looked at him anxiously, and he was only too willing to draw her nearer to scrutinize her features.

What he saw was a face full of character, with a wide sweet mouth. The dark eyes were revealing their thoughts, trying to read his own expression. She had a good skin, clear of all blemishes, with a faultless bone construction. Jeremy held her chin while he made his leisurely examination. She did not evade him, merely waiting until he had concluded. He was so intent on studying her that he forgot to answer her question. He bent and kissed the lovely mouth again with infinite tenderness.

"Well?"

"What was it you asked me?"

"If the scars showed?"

"No, they don't. What I see I like very

43

much. Maybe you are a little paler, but that is understandable."

She laughed ruefully. "I've always liked living in the country."

"And you like *me* very much?" He wanted to hear the words again.

"Yes, I do. I love you and like you. I'm glad you know all about me and there are no secrets between us. I don't want to start with secrets, do you? If you have any you'd better bring them out and we'll make a bonfire of them."

He stirred. "Secrets are not like that. They evade you . . ."

"I suppose so, but I'm in the mood to start from scratch."

"I know. Put the other part of your life right away, out of sight for ever. Don't brood on it, or it'll keep it alive."

"That's what Deborah said," she told him more tranquilly.

He drew a deep breath of contentment. "Look round you, darling. Isn't it good to be here? Tomorrow we'll be married . . . and live happily ever after . . ."

She smiled, narrowing her eyes against the brilliance of the scene confronting them. The lake was so still that not a murmur reached them. It was lifeless beneath the subjugation of the sun. The reflections were magnificent. "It's so big —there is so much more of everything than one could imagine."

"Yes, plenty of room," he agreed. He bent to look into her face as he added: "I'd like plenty of children playing around the ranch some day, darling. How do you feel about that?"

"How many is plenty?" she asked, slightly alarmed.

"Half a dozen at least . . ."

"That's a large family for these days, isn't it?"

"I like large families—and think of the size of the place."

"I am—but that's not the only thing to be taken into account. I feel that four would be plenty—just a nice family you could push around without feeling desperate."

He smiled, meeting her amused glance, for he was pleased with what she said.

"Just so long as you feel that way. It'll be interesting living the way we want to live, being together, having children of our own. I'm all for it, darling."

Soon afterwards he took her back to the house, and they sat for a while on the verandah chatting to Mrs. Dell, over a cup of tea. Jeremy lingered, until Sylvia rose, amused by his reluctance to leave.

"If you don't go soon, dear, I'll never have time for all the things I must do tonight. I've a wedding on my hands in the morning—did you know? Will you be there?"

"I may be—I'll see," he teased. "It might be a good idea." He said good-bye to Mrs. Dell and Sylvia walked with him to the gate. "What things have you to do?"

"A little washing and ironing, and some shoes to clean. I want to wash and set my hair, too. Endless things after the journey . . . and before our wedding."

"Your hair looks wonderful the way it is now."

"Thank you, sir, but you might not like me if I didn't give it the usual attention."

"I wonder. I'm the luckiest man in the world tonight—and the happiest. Oh, Sylvia."

Gaiety left them in sudden longing. "I hope you'll always be able to say that."

"I will. Good night, darling. I'll call for you in the morning. Be ready."

She realized that the deep feeling they shared made them uncertain. They had so much and were afraid to lose it. Her deepening love gave her added understanding of Jeremy's need, and her smile was thoughtful as she stood waving to him from the little gate.

The future might take them out of their depth but they had found one another.

2

JEREMY had decided on a camping honeymoon, but overnight he changed his mind. Sylvia's delicacy had surprised him, and he decided to take her to Banff where, amid supremely beautiful surroundings and in the luxury of a first-class hotel, they might begin their married life.

They each walked warily during those early days. As Sylvia pointed out, they did not know each other very well.

"What I know of you I like exceedingly," he told her. "If there is anything I don't like I won't know it."

She laughed derisively at his sententious tone. "You're in love, but I'm glad you are. Makes life so easy."

"Is that why you married me—for an easy life?"

"Oh, no, I married you for your money."

"Really, darling?"

She went into his arms. "No. You know it's not true."

"It couldn't be, for I haven't enough to tempt anyone. We've got to work for what we want. How about that?"

"Yes—I'll work for you," she promised.

"You sound like a Crusader. There won't be any need to take in washing. Just look after me and I'll be satisfied."

Sylvia had always been careful about her personal appearance and now she revelled in the feeling of affluence that Morgan's money brought her. Her clothes were all of good quality, and chosen with an eye to the future. There was a sophistication about her that puzzled Jeremy sometimes.

"Where did you pick it up—the sophistication, I mean?" He watched her as she stood in front of the mirror one morning, doing her hair.

Her dark eyes were amused. "Perhaps it was always there, in the way you hide your light under a bushel. Do I seem strange to you—I don't want to."

"Not strange—just another delightful surprise in discovering the real you."

"Um!" She glanced through the mirror

into his eyes, and they smiled. His arms went round her gently.

"You're kind of nice." He gave into every slightest whim of hers, delighting in indulging her. In spite of the sorrow in the past there was nothing hard about her and he appreciated that. She was impulsive and loving and he had gained her full confidence. The feeling between them was delicate and neither dare name it in case some of the bloom should be brushed from it. They were intensely happy.

It was over the legacy from Morgan that they had their first serious disagreement.

"I want to buy all my own clothes," Sylvia told him. She had purchased several small articles in Banff for each of them.

"You're my wife and must spend my money—that's understood," Jeremy argued seriously. "Are you insinuating that I can't clothe you?"

"Don't be ridiculous, darling." Her troubled glance met his.

"Then you must spend *my* money, Sylvia. How much do you want?" There was a note of warning in his deep voice and she felt the first pang of dismay.

"But Jeremy . . . when I have this . . ."

"Save your money. There may be a rainy day. Why spend it now?"

"I can't see any harm in spending a little —it's mine."

"Not on your clothes, or anything to do with our joint lives. I won't allow it if I know it. Sorry if I'm dogmatic but I feel a thing about it, Sylvia."

"Oh, dear, I'm sorry you feel this way."

"Don't worry about it—just keep your money . . . you plutocrat." In spite of his jesting tone she saw that the idea displeased him and she let the matter drop. She realized that he disliked all mention of Morgan, too. Was he jealous of that former marriage? She realized that he must be, although he had not actually said so. She was unwilling to mention Morgan's name at any time, but now the knowledge of his displeasure brought a fresh sense of shock and fear. Was it just that they were not fully adjusted yet? Would he change when they had settled down and he had grown more sure of her? They were unanimous in not wishing to recall any association with her former husband. She pondered the cause but could not find any solution. One day they would be obliged to be frank with each other about Morgan.

The happiness that was growing between them ousted any feeling of constraint and she tried to put the matter out of her mind.

"I wonder if anyone ever had a happier honeymoon than ours?" she asked.

"One gets the honeymoon one wants," he told her.

They were both good walkers, and Jeremy saw to it that all walks were within her scope, for she tried to do anything he could do, uncomplaining until she was on the point of collapse. After the first few days he began to understand her mood.

"Oh, I'm wiry. I'm never ill. I had a check-up a few weeks ago and there is nothing wrong with me. I'm quite over the breakdown now, Jeremy."

He drew her close to his side as they walked along the track. "I was looking forward to being married to you, but it's different from what I thought . . ."

"In what way?"

"I don't know that I can put it into words. I'm responsible for you in a way I never thought I'd feel. I'm constantly thinking ahead for you, planning ways to keep you happy, wondering if I can keep this feeling high between us as it is now. Oh, it's lots of fun, but there's more to it than that."

"I feel the same way," she admitted.

"It's no longer just what I want that counts, nor only what you want, but something we both want. I'm starting to ramble, darling, but I know what I mean."

Under his bracing kindness Sylvia was expanding like a flower in the sunshine. She was often gay and audacious, making him laugh tenderly at her sallies. He enjoyed her frequent hesitations, or when she imposed her will on his in some way. She would stand in front of him, her dark head on one side, and say: "I'm going swimming today—what are you doing?"

She would have been instantly deflated had he said he was staying indoors to read a book, but he invariably met her wishes. He knew that her hesitancy sprang from that lost inner self-reliance, and in a cautious way he helped her to rebuild it.

The hotel appealed to them both, and they enjoyed the perfect service, the lovely rooms in their gracious setting, the wonderful views from every window, the gardens with their cheerful flowers. The mountains were still capped with snow.

"We'll never forget this holiday," she prophesied one day as they returned from a pony trip which had taken them into new territory. They had camped out overnight and with three other guests had enjoyed the break from routine. They were to return home next day.

"Do you wish you could stay here for ever?" Jeremy asked.

"No. I'm looking forward to starting our real life together at the ranch."

"Do you want Dan to stay on?" Already Jeremy was beginning to make plans.

"Yes—if you do. He's not doing any harm, is he?"

"Dear Uncle Dan . . ." Jeremy was in a pleasantly relaxed mood.

"I wonder why he's so anxious to stay?"

"He must have his reasons—it'll be interesting to discover them."

It was dusk when they entered the hotel. Sylvia sat down on an easy chair by the window, her dark gaze seeking the superb view. She often sat here while she waited for Jeremy to shave, or to come up from the gardens. He drifted towards her now and sat on a low stool close to her, leaning against her knees. For several minutes they mused as they watched the scintillating colours that came with the brief sunset.

"Home tomorrow, Jeremy."

"Yes." His voice was content. "I like to hear you call it that."

"Jeremy . . . we haven't discussed anything yet, seriously, I mean. I wonder if we should now? There's so much I want to know." Her voice held a pleading note.

She felt him go quiet against her. "No point in bringing all that back to life . . ."

"If we could talk—openly, I believe I'd feel better about it at once."

"Well—what do you want to know?" He spoke grudgingly.

"I've often wondered why you were so interested in me—right from our first meeting, I mean. I felt your interest before Morgan introduced us. You came in and . . ."

He moved sharply. "Sorry, I got cramp . . ."

"I've wanted to ask you before. Then

55

that second time you called when Morgan was out, and you took me to dinner . . . and later you said you wouldn't call again unless he was there."

"Did you want me to?"

"No. I had not asked you then," she spoke warmly. "But I felt your interest."

"I was—just interested to know the sort of woman Morgan had married. I wanted to know if you were happy with him. He was an odd sort of fellow in some ways."

Her gaze followed his through the wide window to the flaming sunset spreading across the sky. Every neutral shade was deepening into ephemeral beauty.

"What business was it of yours?" she asked mildly.

"What a strange question. Call it curiosity if you like. You know—a pal gets married and you wonder what sort of a wife he's chosen." Jeremy had his back to her and he was starting to smoke. "When I got to know you—on the second meeting anyhow—I soon realized why I was interested in you. Let's leave it at that, shall we? I kept out of your way—and it's finished with."

Reason told her to accept his brusque

ruling, but she realized that he was not being entirely frank with her. There was so much in the past that she did not know about both Morgan and Jeremy. Had he always been jealous of Morgan?

"I've always felt that although you professed to be his friend, you did not like Morgan." She looked at him questioningly.

"Isn't that because he was your husband?" he asked in a strained voice. "Am I not entitled to feel a certain amount of jealousy? I'm not proud of it, Sylvia, but that's what's there. Accept the position, then let's forget it ever existed."

She stared at his broad back, knowing he was resenting her questions. He would not put a stop to her deductions, and she pondered just what was the truth.

"I've always felt terribly responsible for the accident that caused Morgan's death. It was a shock and I can't put it from my mind . . ." She longed to be able to tell him what Morgan's mother had said on that terrible night, but he would not understand. His mood would not brook this final shock. He could not see into her mind to realize its hurt, all the implications behind the bitter reproachful indictment.

"Why worry about it any longer? You're going to spoil what we have now if there is much more of it. Do you mind?"

She was turned back on herself, on the confession that trembled on her lips. Jeremy did not want to know anything further regarding the situation.

"Were you with him when his accident happened?" she whispered.

"The plate he wore in his head? Not actually, but we all knew about it, of course. He got that at the end of the war. Look, Sylvia, in some ways it's not easy following Morgan and it's best if we both try to forget the past."

"I want to—more than anything," she stammered.

He began to caress her, kissing her several times, trying to turn her thoughts from the trouble in her mind. "You believe me don't you?" he asked on an afterthought, sensing her shrinking movement.

"Yes." She longed that there might have been complete frankness between them so that she could have dismissed the matter from her mind as he wished.

"Then what's wrong with us both?"

She comforted him in her turn, rocking his head against her tenderly. She wished they could step out of all that threatened to harm their happiness in each other. Morgan's influence was reaching out and if she were not careful it might spoil the future as it had the past.

"He was never kind or patient, Jeremy. You know what he was . . ."

Jeremy kept moving his face against her as if mutely seeking reassurance, and she tried to give it to him. What was the matter with her? Something in their relationship was changing. Was it her own doubt?

"I love you," he told her. "Whatever else, that's strong and true and real . . . Put all else away, will you?"

"Yes, I'll try. I don't think I want dinner tonight, Jeremy. You go down . . ."

"I'd rather stay with you."

"Please go, Jeremy."

He saw that she wished to be alone, and presently he left her.

She strode about the room, all of the past with its searing blight rolling over her sensitivity, until she felt exhausted. When Jeremy entered the room an hour later she tried to appear composed, but her colour was high. She went to meet him so that he would not see her face.

"Jeremy . . ."

"Oh, lord . . ." his tone was impatient and hard. "You don't need to start explaining. I've been thinking too. Let's forget it."

His jealousy of Morgan closed the way irrevocably, and there could not be complete confidence between them. Nothing now would alter facts.

"I'd get ready for bed if I were you— we've a long journey ahead of us tomorrow." His eyes looked harder than she had ever seen them and she realized with a shock that he was suffering, too. What had his thoughts been as he sat quietly alone among the other guests? He seemed aware of what she was thinking. "I didn't eat. I went for a walk in the garden. Thought you wanted to be alone."

There was infinite tenderness between them that night, and their love rose higher than the thin dividing wall that they both recognized but would not admit. Sylvia tried to appease her own hurt by comforting him. As she lay quietly through a sleepless night she wondered what to do for the best.

"I love him—I know now that I never loved Morgan—yet if I could push back the years I would. I failed Morgan because I didn't love him . . . and he knew . . . he knew."

When she felt more assurance she might be able to convince Jeremy somehow.

The journey from Banff back to the ranch was a fairly long run, and they set off early. They were both quiet for the first hour, until Jeremy lighted his pipe and relaxed visibly.

"Tired?" he asked, blowing out the flame of the match.

"Yes. I think so. I've hardly wakened up yet. I'm grumpy in the morning—did you know?" She smiled at him as she spoke.

"Can't say I've noticed it. How's my temper?"

"One of the best—I'm thankful it is." She spoke warmly.

Morgan's temper had been violent and swift, followed by equally quick repentance. His alternating moods had been hard to bear. In comparison Jeremy was equable and gentle, yet she sensed that beneath his quietness there was something that might be even more violent than Morgan's weakness. She defined the difference—Morgan had been weak—Jeremy was strong. Why am I comparing them, she asked herself in despair. Why can't I put it out of my mind as Jeremy asks me to? It's this that will make him angry in time.

She felt the slight constraint between them, and tried hard to break it down. He aided her, and by noon when they had stopped for a meal they were talking freely. She made him laugh several times, and pretended to a gaiety she was far from feeling. She meant to keep her thoughts to herself in future, in a separate compartment in her mind, where they could not hurt either of them. Jeremy appeared to have forgotten the dissension completely. She would learn to do the same.

They were returning to the ranch together as he had planned it so often in his letters. He looked round at her, smiling contentedly. "Home soon, darling."

They arrived in the cool of the evening. Sylvia looked about her with keen appreciation, for smoke was rising in the still air, there was an aroma of bacon, Dan was standing in the doorway grinning at them, and Bing was fussing about them, showing his teeth in a hideous grin of delight.

"Home . . ." she said.

"Shouldn't I carry you over the threshold or something?"

"Dan . . ." she protested, but he lifted her quickly and strode with her into the cabin, kissing her firmly before setting her down. "Thank you, dear . . ."

"That's an old English custom," he said mildly to Dan.

"Aye . . ." Dan had watched with considerable interest.

Jeremy tweaked her hair, his eyes amused. "You go along—we'll attend to the bags. Down Bing—can't you see we're busy?" He fondled the dog's ears as he spoke. "One of these days I'll get me a real dog, then you'll have a bit of competition, eh?"

"He just won't believe he's ninety-eight," Dan said.

Sylvia glanced back over her shoulder. "Ninety-eight?"

"Aye, they reckon seven years to one of ours. At that rate he's near his centenary." Dan was grinning until his leathery face looked about to split.

Sylvia went into the bedroom to take off her outer coat and hat. Life was changing completely, and she felt much more serious than when she was here before. All day she had been striving to meet Jeremy and she felt that he was disarmed. She glanced at the bed, seeing that it was unmade. It was a double bed and had been built in, constructed of laths lashed across four stout poles that appeared to grow out of the floor or foundations. It was immovable and the first of its kind she had seen. She was diverted, for she had not noticed it on the previous visit.

Jeremy brought in their suitcases. "Your trunks are still over in that corner. I just uncorded them and left them for you to unpack. Everything all right?" He was struck by something in her attitude.

"Odd sort of bed—did you make it?"

"No, it came with the place. It's not so bad. I bought a good mattress and it should be comfortable. I always slept in the small room."

"This certainly is big," she conceded.

"Too big?" He had not yet solved her reaction and was puzzled.

"Oh, no, I like a big room. It's just that bed . . ." She began to laugh and he joined in.

"I'll get the mattress. It's still packed just as it came from the store weeks ago. I wasn't tempting providence . . ."

"Dan has kept everything very clean. Can I spread myself in here about curtains and things? It would take off the bare look."

"Sure. Get whatever you want anywhere about the place. It's up to you now, Sylvia. You know what's needed. Get it—but spend my money, that's all I ask." His jaw hardened on the last words. "This is to be our home and I want it the way you want it. There will be plenty of expenses but

65

I'm not a poor man, and I want you to be content."

"I know—you're awfully sweet, darling." She rubbed her head against his shoulder. "I'll be content." She tried to show him that she was not dissatisfied and for some minutes kept him with her while she praised the various appointments.

"I know—you're prepared to like what I offer—but I want more than that from you. I've been pushed around plenty in my life and I want to settle down now. We're here to stay. Does that sound dogmatic? It's not intended that way. This is the place I own, and without you in it I can't be happy, so it's quite simple. I can provide a decent living for the two of us, and for the children we shall have one day."

The talk had grown serious and she was afraid of where it might lead them but he persisted as if determined to be done with the subject.

"I want you to make friends here; if I could I'd tie you down with bands of steel but only you can do that. I want you to stay because you like it. Pleasing me might grow thin in time—I don't want that angle. Where you go, I'm going; just remember that, will you? When you are deciding you're deciding for the two of us. Right?"

"Your whole interest is here . . ." she said thoughtfully.

"Yes—if you are here. Without you it wouldn't mean anything to me. Can't explain it nearer than that." He spoke cheerfully, but she felt the weight behind his words. Jeremy was making the position clear at the outset.

"Thank you, Jeremy. You're a darling, and I'll do my share. This can be anything we make of it. I feel happy about it, too."

He put her aside. "Then we'll leave it there. I just wanted to get it straight at the start of our life together. There's no turning back for us."

What did he fear, she pondered. She spoke soberly: "I think I understand."

"Right—now where were we?" He turned from the conversation as deliberately as if he had said all he would on the matter. For the first time for several days she noticed the limp in his gait. It only showed when he was tired. This was the legacy he would carry to his grave. She felt that he needed her and the knowledge helped her to meet the situation. He relied on her more than he knew. She kissed him, pretending an energy she did not possess.

"Let's eat. Dan will think we're not hungry if we keep him waiting any longer. Oh, doesn't it smell good?" They entered the living-room, arm in arm, and the seriousness slid off Jeremy. He went through into the kitchen and washed his hands at the sink there.

"We could run a pipe into the bedroom and have a sink there," he called. "It would be useful."

Sylvia agreed, and they were soon seated at the table enjoying the excellent fare that Dan had provided. Beside the bacon and vegetables, there was corn on the cob which Sylvia had not tasted before. She picked up a cob as she saw the others doing and ate with relish the soft golden balls. The pumpkin pie was also new to her, heavily flavoured with nutmeg, but she enjoyed it very much. Dan was gratified when he saw them enjoying the meal. The coffee was black because there was no milk.

"We could get a goat," Jeremy half promised. "Or I might get milk from the village. We've not bothered, but you'll want milk, won't you?"

"Yes, I can't drink tea without it—and I like tea, too."

She and Jeremy worked until bedtime, unpacking, preparing, planning their programme of work for the future. There was no time or inclination to look around outside.

"It can wait," Jeremy yawned. "I'll show you round tomorrow."

Sylvia slid down into the great bed. Jeremy reached out for her. The quietness was so intense that she felt its weight on the cabin roof. This was her first experience of sleeping at the ranch and the complete silence felt unnatural and elemental. The hotel sounds at Banff had been subdued but lively, and had not prepared her for this brooding silence. She listened intently for the movement of the trees but there was no wind, the night was soundless and remote.

She fell asleep before it had power to trouble her and slept for some hours, waking in that curious half light before dawn comes to the earth. She slid out of Jeremy's arms without disturbing him and made her way to the window. She thought of her journey across the continent; of the never ceasing roar of London's traffic. All that was in the past. This was the brave new world to which she would grow accustomed in time. Her heart ached as she leaned against the window casing. A rush of cool sweet air greeted her, for Jeremy believed in open windows. She tried to steady her racing thoughts. The air was filled with perfume from the garden, and she closed her eyes trying to realize all the implications of her presence here.

I'll kill you—before I'll let you leave me . . . you'll never get away. The words were so loud and strong that she glanced around, expecting to see Morgan towering above her in the gloom. She shrank against the wall, trembling. *You'll never get away.*

She heard the movement Jeremy made as he strode out of bed. Her lightly balanced mind accepted the reality instantly, and with relief. "I suspected this," he said.

"I'm sorry if I disturbed you, darling. It's just the newness. I'm not used to such

70

a quiet place." She spoke as if trying to appease him. His sane presence cast aside that terrifying shadow that haunted her.

He put his arm about her waist as they watched the dawn. "Aren't you happy with me?"

"Oh, yes. Don't let's discuss it, darling. I am happy. How could it be otherwise with you? I love you so dearly." Her voice was deep and utterly beautiful as it broke on the gentle words. Jeremy drew her closer, sighing a little.

"Nothing can hurt you from the past if you don't let it. Don't spoil what we have. Do you want to talk?"

"No. I was just looking." How could she tell him of what had been in her mind for those lonely moments when Morgan had reached out to touch her again? The bitter finality of that quarrel was only equalled by his mother's words later, when she said with acid coldness: *I shall for ever hold you morally responsible for Morgan's death. You and I will always know . . .* Jeremy wouldn't understand that these things had eaten into the fabric of her life. His admitted jealousy did nothing to help the situation either. She could only suffer silently, for it was too close and personal and confusing.

Jeremy's face was grim in the half light, but he said no word of rebuke. She turned towards him, feeling his warmth and strength. She knew that her reticence was hurting him, yet she could not break the silence without harming him further.

"Let's go back to bed. You'll get a chill," he said.

In the morning she helped to prepare the breakfast. She was determined to shoulder her share of the work. She was, however, not used to the fact that a fire had to be lighted in the stove before water could be boiled for a cup of tea. Dan had plenty of wood chopped in readiness and it was not a formidable business. Jeremy soon had the stove drawing, and when the kettle boiled they made tea.

"The best cup I ever tasted," she said in surprise. They were young and their spirits rose after they had eaten. This was their first day together in their own home.

"Leave the table . . ." Jeremy said imperatively as they finished breakfast.

"Come outside. I want to show you round."

After putting down some scraps for Bing she followed him to the door. Jeremy put an arm about her shoulders.

"Darling, this is just to keep you from forgetting that I love you very much." He kissed her with deep passion. "When you get around to it you can tell me the same."

She smiled into his eyes, and they went out together. The sun was high, its brilliance lying beneficently over the sloping land that stretched and yawned and expanded as if awaking to another day. The garden immediately round the cabin was full of colour and she saw where the perfume she had noticed through the bedroom window had come from. The beds were full of old-fashioned flowers and shrubs. She preferred flowers with perfume. Jeremy drew her on, impatient to be out of the garden. They followed the path away from the cabin through the acres of healthy fruit bushes which she knew would be their main source of income for some years to come. To her inexperienced eyes everything looked to be trim and neat. Already much of the fruit was beginning to ripen.

Suddenly, where the bushes stopped on the very edge of the land, she drew in her breath sharply, for she had not been as far as this before. Jeremy had certainly not prepared her for this.

They were standing so high that they were able to see the tremendous length of lake, the mountains unable to dwarf its size. Trees and mountains were reflected solemnly and perfectly until it was almost impossible to distinguish reality from reflection. The opposite shore showed brown and barren, where a forest fire had devastated and scarred it the previous year. There were no cabins on that side, and little beach either.

Closer at hand, on the shore above which they stood, she could see reeds standing as high as a man. The ground sloped down more smoothly to this beach, broken only by the main road which wound round the lake for several miles. There was utter privacy about the location.

Her eyes shone as she turned back to Jeremy, who had been watching her quietly.

"I'd no idea it was like this. It's the loveliest place I've ever seen—and it's yours . . . amazing."

"Ours," he corrected. "Right down to the beach. Glad you like it, darling. It's what I meant last night when we were talking. There's safety here for you as well as for me. Some day when we're calmer we'll talk about it. Let's just accept what *is*. Look along that ridge to the right of the cabin—know what I'm planning for that ridge?"

She looked carefully along the rocky site that jutted far out over the lake, giving an unequalled outlook in every direction. A few trees grew solidly, bent by the winds, their tremendous height greater than one could assess from a distance.

"A. . . a hotel?" she hazarded. "It is a perfect place for a hotel, I think."

"You guessed right, but the hotel must wait. We'd need real money for that. I thought we'd build a few cabins and run a sort of super auto camp. How does the idea strike you?"

"Wonderful. Let me help with that. I'd love something like that."

"I'll need your help," he spoke simply.

"Listen—this is it, if you agree. The fruit is our first consideration, but we can employ labour for the busy periods. We can build half a dozen cabins, there is a natural source of water right at the site which only needs piping in. We might buy an electric motor and run our own plant for electricity. We'd equip the cabins fully, hoping to attract the better class type of tourist, the sort who will come for a whole summer and not mind the bills! It will cost a bit at first, but the outlay would be justified."

"What sort of summers have you here?" she asked, musing.

"Splendid. Long, hot days, only an occasional storm. We could expand the vegetable garden for fresh produce and sell them to the guests perhaps."

"A lot of work—but fun," Sylvia agreed. "I could cook. Let's plan a communal dining-room with kitchen attached. Oh, Jeremy, that's it. Let them all come to ready-cooked meals in the dining-room. It would be attractive and comfortable, although you could fix up arrangements for them to make tea and so on in their cabins. I can cook—I'm quite a good cook, really."

"But I don't want you tied to a kitchen stove all day," he remonstrated.

"We can always get help later if we see it will work."

He agreed doubtfully. "Then you like the idea?"

"Oh, yes. What made you think of it?"

"Just that there seems to be a need for that sort of thing along this lake. I could do most of the work on the cabins myself and save expense—perhaps get a plumber and a builder to get me started." He was striding near to the site which they had been viewing from a distance. On this higher ridge the air was cool and crisp. The ridge was as flat as a frying pan and almost as round; the handle of the pan sloped back to join the mainland that led directly to their own cabin.

"I really like it better than where we are," Jeremy mused. "The cabin was built when I took over or else it would have been my idea to build where the view is. Still, we can't live on the view. I guess it's more snug in the cold weather the way it is."

"If the cabins are a bit exposed it won't

matter, because they'll only be used in the summer." Sylvia could find no flaw in the scheme, and already the cabins were rising in her mind's eye and she was furnishing them. "Could we have . . . ?"

"Furnishing them will be *your* job, Sylvia. I'll give you a cheque when the time comes and leave the choice to you."

She flushed, and then the colour receded from her face. Jeremy's kindness was sometimes more than she could bear. He made her feel that she counted, and it was a wonderful new security. She paced back and forth with him as they measured and planned.

While they were so engaged Dan came across the pan handle, as Sylvia mentally called it, and greeted them cheerfully. He did not look quite so old this morning.

"You staying out here all day?" he demanded.

"No—just making plans." Jeremy outlined what was in their minds, while Dan shrewdly followed his pointing hand.

"Say, you've got something there. If you have the cash it'll be a money-spinner."

"Think so?" For all his good nature Jeremy was not easily swayed by the approval of another, but he was pleased that Dan liked their ideas.

"I could help," Dan suggested tentatively.

"Are you intending staying around these parts?"

Dan's faded eyes flashed up to meet his. "Sure. For the rest of my life."

"All right. You can help. There will be plenty for all of us."

Sylvia had not interrupted the conversation between the two men, and she smiled when Dan braced his thin shoulders. She knew that he breathed easier, for he had not known what to expect from them. She realized that her own wish had decided Dan's future, and it gave her a feeling of pleasure to know that Jeremy had tried to please her.

"Jeremy now has two willing helpers, a brand new scheme, and a future. What more could anyone want?" she asked.

"We'll build a hotel one day," Jeremy promised as they walked back to the cabin together. Dan pointed out where he had kept the kitchen garden under control. He liked to be appreciated and usually saw to it that he got what he wanted.

"I'm going down to the store," Jeremy said. "We need provisions. Coming?"

"I'll have a bite to eat ready when you get back," Dan offered.

"Be careful of the butter in case we can't get any more today," Sylvia warned.

Dan's face was a study and she could not determine its expression.

"Was he pleased or not?" she asked Jeremy as they swung down the lane, hand in hand. He was limping again but she did not comment.

"Dan? Just relieved, I imagine. You have a way of making him feel one of the family that pleases him. I predict that we shall never again be able to shake Dan out of our lives."

They started to laugh as they left the lane and merged on to the road. "Who cares? Oh, we're happy, aren't we? I like it here . . ." She bent swiftly, lifting his clasped hand in hers, and kissed his knuckles.

He stopped on the road. "Hey, what is this?" He was smiling broadly, however, pleased with her impulsive action.

She coloured. "Oh, you said when I could get round to it some time . . ."

"Come here . . ."

She was off, running swiftly along the road, laughing as she heard him overtaking her. When they had exchanged kisses they walked on more soberly, along the shaded tree-bordered road to the store.

"After all, we must remember we're an old married couple now . . ." he said, grinning.

In six weeks time most of their plans had taken definite shape. Sylvia was surprised to find how easily and rapidly everything slipped into place. Jeremy found that with the help of a local builder from Nelson, he and Dan could make the framework of each cabin in under a week. There was no difficulty over supplies and the work progressed rapidly.

Jeremy did not work to a time schedule, but simply from dawn until dusk. He was intensely interested, intent on having some returns for his labour that summer if possible. They made six cabins, roofing them with shingle. The weather was calm. Dan proved to be a carpenter of sorts, and his interest now fully aroused, he worked with Jeremy, his slowness more than compensated by his staying power. Jeremy left him to it, letting the old man finish the details in each cabin, while he and the builder got on with the heavier work. Jeremy took the brunt of every job. He was now very brown, his hair bleaching in the sun, his blue eyes thoughtful.

Sylvia cooked all their meals, and kept the cabin clean. She worked out a colour scheme for each cabin interior, and measured for what furniture would be needed. They all felt to be working against time and she wondered why it was so important to them. They should have been able to relax, but neither she nor Jeremy had the desire for that. They were so busy that they scarcely had time to meet during the day.

At breakfast one morning Jeremy gave her an open cheque to cover the soft furnishings, and other things they had decided would be needed.

"Do you want me to go along with you?" he asked. "Could you manage alone?"

"If you're busy I can manage. Could I go to Vancouver instead of Nelson? There would be a much wider choice."

"Please yourself about that." Only half his attention was on what she was saying. "I'm certainly busy, and if you could manage alone it would help. Go where you can get the best value for the money."

"I'd better go today, hadn't I? Dan can cook the meals while I'm away. You won't feel it's breaking in on your time then, will you?" Sylvia looked forward to the brief change at the coast. The knowledge that Jeremy trusted her absolutely and relied on her taste, helped her a lot, and she decided not to be side-tracked in any way from her own decision.

He came down to Locker to see her off on the coach on which she would travel to Nelson on the first part of the journey. From there she would go to the coast by train.

"Around eight hundred miles," Jeremy said thoughtfully. "It's just occurred to me that this will be our first parting. Maybe I'd better come with you. I don't know that I'm keen on your wandering around Vancouver alone."

"No. You have too much to do. I shall manage, because I want to manage. Don't you see? It's terribly important to me to carry this through."

"I see a very determined young woman intent on getting her own way. I also think I see someone with a happy light in her eyes." He was smiling broadly.

"Oh, yes, I wondered if you'd notice that. In all my life I've never been as happy as I am now."

"Work helps, doesn't it?" he agreed quietly. "I believe we're getting used to being happy . . . together . . ."

"If we are it's a wonderful thing. I'm grateful for it . . ."

He put his brown finger against her lips. "Gratitude is forbidden between us."

She kissed his fingers, for there was not time for more conversation as the coach hove round the bend in the road. Jeremy swung up his arm to stop it, and Sylvia prepared to step up into it. Jeremy kissed her, to the delight of the few persons who were watching them with considerable interest. He swung up her small case.

"When will you be back?"

"Saturday morning at the latest—sooner if I can."

She waved to him as he stood bareheaded in the middle of the road. She might have been just any housewife going off for a few days, leaving her husband alone, but she knew there was more to it than that. She strained her eyes to see him as long as she could.

Nelson was no preparation for the busy life in Vancouver. Sylvia was glad to have something definite in her mind, and she plunged into an orgy of buying and spending in the busy stores. Until that was safely accomplished she would not permit herself to relax. She visited each store in turn, buying sheets, blankets, spreads, pillow-cases, towels, table linen, cushions, pillows, and other soft furnishings. She saw to it that these were despatched by rail and road. Furniture was more of a problem but she finally settled on six sets of economically-priced bedroom furniture, many of the pieces being convertible for day-time living. These she paid for and also had despatched the same day. Then came the kitchen ware, and finally the lounge furniture which was to serve in a communal way for all the cabins. She followed her colour schemes and finally made a choice. When all was complete she gave herself a day in which to visit points of interest in the city.

It was June and Vancouver was at its loveliest. She went through Stanley Park as far as Siwash rock, revelling in the luscious greens and browns of the trees, the thick grass underfoot like a carpet, the flowers, the Totem poles. Everything was strange and utterly delightful. Save for her honeymoon this was her first holiday for years, and she enjoyed every moment of the day. She dallied along the waterfront, seeing the lions guarding the entrance to the harbour, admiring the lovely lines of the coast. Often now she wished that Jeremy were with her, but she enjoyed even his absence, for she took time to meditate on their happiness from afar.

She walked for miles along the tree-bordered streets, amazed by the beauty of the gardens which were without fencing of any kind. Most of them had velvety lawns that sloped down to the wide pavements, with flowers growing nearer the houses. That walk gave her a better idea of Vancouver than any other she could have taken. She had no knowledge of the miles she must have walked, but she was certainly tired when she recrossed the bridge and made her way along Granville Street for a meal. She was longing for a cup of tea. All day her thoughts had been in abeyance, for she was interested in everything, but as she sat down in a cafe, she felt a sudden nostalgia from which she recoiled.

Sitting a few tables away from her was a man who reminded her strongly of Morgan. He had Morgan's arrogant movement of the head, his dark, crisp hair, his tallness from the waist. The illusion was so complete that her hands shook and her fascinated gaze was held. Suddenly he turned his face towards her, and she saw that the resemblance was incomplete. This man was built in a softer mould, his expression different, his eyes those of a stranger. Full-face he did not even faintly resemble Morgan. But the first shock lingered on in her and thrust her back into the past with one sharp stab.

She tried to eat the meal she had ordered, to interest herself in the others who were talking and meeting, and living their lives at the other tables. She was over-tired and it would have been wiser to shorten her walk and come in for a meal earlier.

A woman came along the busy rows of tables, questing for a seat. Sylvia smiled at her, nodding across to the vacant chair opposite. The stranger dropped into it with a sigh of thankfulness.

"Isn't it warm? I was afraid I wouldn't manage to find a seat as it's so late."

"It *is* hot," Sylvia agreed, glad of her company. She studied her companion, who looked about thirty-four or thirty-five. She was good-looking, expensively dressed, her hair beautifully done. She looked the completely self-possessed young matron.

"I'm up from Port Moody to shop for my children. Two birthdays in less than a week and we always give a courtesy gift to the other one."

"Three children? You're lucky," Sylvia said, smiling.

"All boys, too."

"Would you have liked a girl?"

"I don't know. One takes what comes." She laughed as if amused at her thoughts. "Charles is eight, Patrick six, and Tony nearly five. They drive me mad sometimes."

"I'm sure they do."

"Have you any?"

"No." Sylvia met her gaze blankly, feeling a warmth of interest that surprised her. She spoke a little of her life, careful not to reveal too much, but glad to give the confidence. "I don't suppose you are interested . . ."

"Oh, but I am. Sometimes it's fun to talk to strangers, too. You'll settle down when you have children, but this must seem a great change from your life in England. I'm Janet Borrow."

"I'm Sylvia Lang. We're living on Kootenay Lake."

"I've never been there. What's it like?" she paused. "I've been to Harrison Hot Springs—something like that perhaps?"

"Yes. I imagine so. It's rather magnificent. We've been too busy to explore much yet but we will after next week." Sylvia paused.

"What happens next week? You intrigue me." Janet waited for a reply. She was unable to classify Sylvia by any of her known standards and she waited for some revealing glimpse of her background. Why was she here alone?

"Next week we are opening an auto camp for summer guests. We've built half a dozen cabins and I've been buying the necessary equipment for them here. It was my husband's idea. He hopes to make enough money to build a hotel one day." She went on to describe what had been done.

"Sounds wonderful," Janet agreed. She sighed and looked down into her cup of tea. "I wish everything in my life was as straight forward as that. My trouble is something I can't get round at all. Sometimes I wish I could go to sleep for a hundred years so that I needn't know the pain . . ."

Sylvia waited, her dark eyes alight with sympathy. "Don't tell me if it hurts."

"I'd like to tell you. We're strangers, and will never meet again probably, but we can think of each other sometimes. My husband is dying . . . just that. He's fading out of life slowly and surely with every day that comes."

"Oh, no," Sylvia whispered. "What's wrong?"

"He has curvature of the spine, through an accident when he was a child. When we married I knew he might not live long, but we took a chance. I'd every opportunity to back out if I'd wanted but I loved him—and I still love him. I wish you knew him. He's one of the loveliest faces I've ever seen."

Her emotion was deep and genuine, and utterly without affectation. Sylvia did not speak.

"We decided to have children—so that I wouldn't be lonely—one day. Now the time is coming; he thinks I don't realize how near it is, but I do. We're both trying to hold it away from us . . ."

"Is it quite inevitable?" Sylvia spoke gently.

"Yes." Janet snapped shut her handbag decisively. "Strange, isn't it? I've everything in life I could possibly want—save the only thing I truly want and need. I don't think I can bear it when Gabriel goes . . . yet, I know I will have to. There are the children to think of—he wants them to be fine persons. I'll work for that—Oh, God, what's the use of pretending? I shan't care when he's gone. How can I stand it alone? How can I?" Her eyes were full of tears as she threw out the despairing question.

"Have you relatives?" Sylvia felt the question was inadequate, for relatives could not help at such a time. No one could come near enough to the perfect relationship that existed between a man and woman who loved each other. She was amazed at her own understanding. This must be something Jeremy had taught her during their short time together.

"Yes. We've done everything." Janet turned her head impatiently. "It's not an ordinary illness that could be cured with drugs."

There was a short silence between them. Sylvia gathered her thoughts together to try to help, feeling sorry for the woman facing her. "I was reading of someone who faced a similar situation—she went to an Indian reservation somewhere—and found perfect health after a time." She spoke idly, almost absently, realizing that it could not help Janet. Suddenly she held out her hand. "Janet—that's the answer for you. Why don't you do something like that? Go away to some place where you can find health for him. There must be lots of healthy places—the Kootenays, for instance . . ."

"Your place?" Janet's attention focussed on her suddenly.

"Not particularly. The whole Kootenay district is so healthy that you can scarcely go wrong. I'm sure I feel better through living there. Oh, the air is so fresh and pure blowing over the mountains. Jeremy thinks it may feel cold to me in the winters, but ours is a summer camp. It might do your husband good. I wouldn't know. It's an idea."

"It certainly is. I wonder if that's why we had to meet today?" The question lay unanswered, but they looked at one another with a new awareness. "Tell me more."

They talked eagerly until the café emptied. Sylvia was the first to come back to realization of her surroundings. "We've outstayed our welcome. Shall we go?"

"Yes. I wish you could come with me to Port Moody. Is it quite out of the question?"

"I'm afraid so. I must catch the night train," Sylvia told her.

"Yes, and I've a million things to do. Meeting you feels to have invigorated my whole outlook. I'm not going to sit down and wait for something to happen. I begin to have faith that Gabriel will get well again. If only he can . . . You can definitely expect us on Thursday of next week. We shall want two cabins—one for the children as they will sleep apart from us."

"Won't you need to consult your husband first?" Sylvia was a little troubled by the impulsive speed of the arrangements.

"No, he'll come when he knows I wish it. He doesn't work. His one hobby is his violin. He's a fine musician." Janet's abstracted air had vanished completely.

"I hope we aren't making a mistake— that you'll like the place . . ."

"Don't worry—it won't matter. Nothing matters any longer save Gabriel. Don't get scared. Give me your full address."

They parted at the door of the café, each going a different way. Sylvia hoped she had not been indiscreet, and wondered if Jeremy would be willing to accept someone in the camp about whom he knew nothing. If Janet and her family only stayed a week it could not matter. Before going to the depot to catch her train, Sylvia went into a store to order many extravagant luxuries in the way of tinned foods. Gabriel's appetite might need tempting. How wonderful if they could help to restore him to health.

The return journey to Nelson passed quickly, for she had much on which to cogitate. Jeremy was waiting for her when the train drew in early the following morning. She saw his face light up when he recognized her, and he strode along beside the slowly-moving train until it halted. His face was cool and hard against hers when he kissed her. He held her close for a moment.

"I've missed you . . . it was a mistake to go without me. This week's been the longest in my life. I wonder you could . . ." The reproach made her smile.

"I missed you too, Jeremy. Oh, but you are looking well. This life must suit you for you've never looked better. You're quite handsome . . ."

"You hadn't been gone an hour when I

realized how lonely I was. Don't do it again, darling."

She laughed again at his rueful tone. "Nice of you, but I hoped you would miss me a little." His welcome was so urgent and real that she knew her presence meant much to him. "Those are mine and those . . . I've brought a lot more stuff. Did you get all I sent on?"

"I'll check with you later but I imagine everything has arrived. It's been quite interesting to be at the receiving end. You'll be relieved to know the furniture fits. We unloaded it yesterday."

"Of course it fits. I measured to make sure. Oh, the steamer is waiting—are we going home that way, instead of by coach? That will be interesting."

"Sleep well on the train?" he demanded.

"No. There's something about a night journey that gets me down."

"You were missing me."

She laughed and blushed delightfully. "Jeremy—we've got some customers. They are coming along next Thursday." She told him about her meeting with Janet while they tramped about the deck, as the steamer sailed up the calm lake. "They will come for a week until they see if they like the place—if they do they'll spend the summer with us."

"That's pretty good for a start. Not only do you furnish the cabins, but you fill them too. Seems to me I was right smart when I married you."

There was plenty to discuss on the remainder of the journey. Jeremy had news of his own. The cabins were finished, water laid on, stove installed, and since the furniture had arrived all looked very comfortable.

When Sylvia saw the cabins an hour later she was charmed with their appearance, and sure that they would appeal to holiday-makers. As she stood in the doorway of the last cabin she raised a happy face to Jeremy. He drew her close possessively.

"Did you say you were glad to see *me*?" he complained.

"I'm sure I did. Although you haven't given me much time to say anything of a private nature. We seem to be taken up with business, don't we?"

"We need not be too business-like," he urged.

"Are we? Isn't it just that we don't question the wonderful feeling between us any longer? I'm just thankful that it's there, darling."

"Just so long as I know that you're glad to be back with me . . ."

"I am. Just keep on loving me, Jeremy, for I love you so much."

He sighed, and she felt that her answer had not fully satisfied him. He did not pursue the point, however. "Dan has been the cook while you've been away, but he'll be relieved now you are back. He can't do anything unless it's out of a frying-pan."

They were walking slowly back to their own cabin as he spoke. "I thought men liked frying-pan food best." She bent to speak to Bing who was giving her a great welcome. He followed them, sniffing at their shoes. "Hullo, Dan."

"Yes, but not at every meal," Jeremy said aloud.

"He's just jealous," Dan spoke complacently.

Sylvia knew that they were both trying to show her that they had missed her, and she smiled at them both, seeing them with renewed vision.

The following days were busy ones as they prepared for their first guests. The camp looked neat and not like any other that Jeremy had seen. He wanted it to be individual as well as efficient.

Dan had surpassed himself in the small garden surrounding each cabin. The natural line of the trees added to the attraction of the location.

"We must even have individuality in the cooking," Sylvia agreed as she collected recipes and planned endless menus. "Everything must be original and as good as we can possibly make it."

All was ready down to the final polish on the day that Janet planned to bring her small family.

"I hope they *do* come," Dan said speculatively, glancing over his thin shoulder at Sylvia as he attended to the stove.

3

SYLVIA was aghast at Dan's implied doubt.

"Sometimes folks think better of their promises," he hastened to say. "Maybe these won't. Don't look so worried."

"I'm sure they'll come." Sylvia took the doubt to Jeremy, for this was the first time it had occurred to her that Janet might not keep her word. The promise *had* been made in the emotion of the moment. She might not be able to fulfil it.

"Why care?" Jeremy asked her sensibly. "If not them, we'll get someone else. Don't worry. We'll advertise and that will bring 'em rolling in. It's only the end of June, and the season's just begun."

Sylvia did worry, however, until evening, when she saw a long touring car coming slowly up the lane, heralding its arrival with several piercing blasts of the horn. Jeremy straightened his back in the vegetable patch and strode forward. Sylvia came running from the cabin. Dan stayed where he was, curious and impressed in spite of himself. She'd been right—they'd come. He clicked his tongue at the dog who settled at his feet.

Janet stopped the car and stepped out. She was clad in trousers and yellow sweater. Her beautiful, short hair was thrust back from a moist, harassed face. Three boys sat in the back watching the proceedings owlishly, not moving.

"Thank God this is the right place. We've been asking for miles." Janet turned to Sylvia thankfully. Her manner was nervous. "What a long way it is from the coast. Sylvia—Gabriel is exhausted. He fainted an hour ago. Help me . . . help me . . ."

"Jeremy—please. This is Janet Borrow." Sylvia appealed wordlessly to Jeremy.

Jeremy shook hands, taking in the situation shrewdly. Janet suffered from nervous strain, and her attitude was reflected on the small boys who smiled diffidently at Jeremy. He opened the near door, seeing the tired, hunched figure of their father who appeared to be incapable of leaving the car. The thin white face was beaded with moisture. "Can I help you?" Jeremy said smiling. He was always direct, and Sylvia knew that someone had to get hold of the situation. They could not stand about indefinitely. What a terrible thing to happen.

"Yes, please."

"Gabriel, dear, this is Sylvia's husband. I told you about them." Janet leaned nonchalantly on the open door of the car, nothing in her casual stance to suggest that she had appealed to Sylvia for help.

"A good description, too—I would know you anywhere," Gabriel said in that low, exhausted voice.

Sylvia was alarmed by his look of fragility. Janet must have courage to bring him so far, for he did not appear to have strength to live through the week they planned.

"Gabriel is not feeling too well."

"I'll help you," Jeremy said.

Gabriel was not embarrassed as Jeremy reached in to help him. Sylvia went round to speak to the children. Was it fear that had silenced them, too?

"I can manage, thanks. Just give me

your arm. Janet thinks I'm going to be carried but she is mistaken. I'll walk in on my own two feet." There was a thin gaiety in the low voice that made them all smile with relief. Yet how could they smile when tragedy loomed so close, Sylvia thought.

Jeremy set a slow pace with Gabriel leaning against him. Gabriel was a much smaller man, and the comparison between them was terrible. The two women watched for a moment until clamour broke out among the children.

"Oh, yes—I have three sons, haven't I?" Janet turned in relief. "Sylvia—my sons. They are dirty, tired, hungry, in sad need of chastisement, and I am too depressed to attend to it."

"Let me," Sylvia offered. "Dan, would you help with the baggage, please?"

The old man strolled closer, his face kind and concerned for he had passed the two men and seen Gabriel's face.

"I'll prepare a meal. Come along, boys. I'll show you where you can wash your hands. Let your father rest for a while."

Janet gripped a small case and set off to follow her husband. It was plain to see that she had no other interest at the moment.

Sylvia took the youngest child by the hand and led the way to her own cabin. They could not stand on ceremony tonight, their need was too great for that. It must wait for the morrow. She washed the smallest boy who told her that his name was Tony and that he had brought two engines with him, and he liked tomato sauce. She showed the other boys how to get started before turning to make the coffee.

The children all had fair skins and would have their mother's handsome looks as they grew older. They were docile at the moment because they were both hungry and jaded, but she realized they were spirited children, and foresaw a busy time ahead watching that no harm came to them.

The table was set in the communal dining-room where all meals would be taken in future. Presently Sylvia led the three boys to it. Now that the traces of tears had been removed they were handsome youngsters. She set them to the table at the places they would occupy later, and saw them started on the meal, which was a simple one of ham, salad and fruit. She had filled their cups with hot milk, adding a dash of coffee and sweetening it liberally. She liked the way they settled down to appease their hunger. How long was it since Janet had thought to feed them?

Sylvia prepared a tray with similar food and took it across to Gabriel's cabin. Jeremy was running the big car under cover, and Dan had already removed the bags. What a lot of stuff they had brought with them, she thought absently.

"Come in." Janet's tone was cheerful. "How nice of you to bring something over. You'll not need to go to the dining-room now, Gabriel."

"How are you?"

Gabriel was propped up in bed, with a fur rug thrown over him. Now that she could see him, with the pain gone from his white face she realized that Janet had not erred in describing his face as beautiful. There was pain in it yet, but subdued and hidden. He was as anxious as Janet to make light of his plight.

"I'm better. I think the journey was too long. After all, eight hundred miles would be an effort at any time, and I've not been well lately."

Janet placed the tray across his knees, shaking out a small table napkin and pushing it under his chin.

A flash of amusement passed between them. "I will not be treated as if I were one of your small sons," he grumbled.

"No? By the way, how are they?" Janet spoke on an afterthought.

"Eating large quantities of food, and considerably cleaner about the face and knees than they were," Sylvia informed them.

They laughed at her tone, but she could see that at the moment it was not the most important matter in their minds. "You go and have your meal," Gabriel suggested. "I can manage quite well now. This looks delicious."

"If you get through all that I shan't think there is much the matter with you." Janet kissed his forehead before following Sylvia from the cabin. "I love this delicate pink shade—so cheerful. Just what I need . . ."

They walked together to the dining-room, and were greeted by an outburst from the three boys. "Mother, Charles says there are bears . . ."

106

"Mother—Pat hurt me . . . he did . . ."

"Mother, Tony keeps putting in a whole slice at a time."

"Well, he shouldn't. Empty your mouth, Tony." Janet spoke absently, but the child obeyed her as if he knew she would see her order carried out. "Oh, what a charming place this is. It's so nice to just *be* here, too. You've given us a lovely welcome, Sylvia. I'll always remember."

Sylvia poured her a large cup of coffee and passed her the salad. The children settled down to keep her company, and they chatted while Janet ate her meal. She appeared more relaxed and soothed. Finally the children offered to put themselves to bed in the new cabin which had been pointed out to them.

"They can," Janet said tiredly. "It helps me a lot. I'll go in later and see they are all right."

The children went out, whispering among themselves in subdued excitement. It was so quiet after they had gone that the two women looked at each other.

"Peace and children do not go together

—ever, but I wouldn't be without mine for a fortune," Janet said huskily.

There was no time for intimate talk that night, for as soon as she had finished her meal Janet jumped up and went to see if the children were all right. She found them all asleep, each having chosen his bed, folded his clothes, and tumbled head first into oblivion.

"Easy consciences," Janet said to her husband. "How do you like it here, dear? Isn't it quiet? I should think you could hear a rumour."

"It'll be all right when we get used to it. There should be plenty of fishing judging by the look of that lake as we came along. Jeremy's got a boat, he tells me."

She could have cried for his courage. "Yes. I think they'll be able to use all the fish they can get, too."

"Did you make sure my violin was safe?" He was undressed and in bed for he was not intending to take a walk that night.

She nodded absently. "Over there, darling. That old man brought it in with the other cases. Oh, but I'm tired. That was quite a journey . . . but oh, the arrival was sweet."

"I'll drive going back," he promised gently.

Their eyes met in the mirror in front of which she was standing. Tears rose like mist in them before she could reply. She busied her shaking hands with her hair so that he would not see. As she brushed her hair her mind grew tranquil and resolute again. They had arrived and the experiment was begun. At least she would not be able to blame herself for not trying.

Dear God—help us now . . .

For everyone on the ranch the following week was strenuous. Sylvia and Jeremy enjoyed the work, for they realized that they were able to meet the demands made upon them. Dan slipped into his place, always there when wanted, absent when not. He was proving to be remarkably understanding, and he often helped out with the children when they drove everyone else to desperation.

Charles, (Sylvia never heard him called anything but Chas by the others, and she gradually did the same) Patrick and Tony kept everyone alert during their wakeful days, although on the whole Janet said they were quiet.

"For them," she conceded. "I suppose they've not yet got used to the distractions you have to offer."

There was no danger for them of passing traffic, for the garden sloped down to the shore, and the privacy of the beach was half its charm. The children revelled in the unaccustomed freedom. Most days they bathed without their swim-suits, simply paddling in and out of the water as the spirit moved them. Their shrill voices could be heard all day long as they shouted to each other. There was always someone around when they played in the lake, for the sake of safety.

Gabriel slowly regained a little strength. He spent most of his time that first week in an easy chair outside his cabin, over-looking the activities of his sons. He was content to watch, while Janet read beside him, or sewed or knitted. Sylvia realized that they were both relaxing.

"This wonderful air *is* doing you good, Gabriel," Janet said critically one day. "Your colour is better—you've a sparkle in your eyes again." She had been studying him before she spoke.

"I know. I feel better. In a couple of days I'm going fishing with Jeremy." His smile was full of content.

The long days were filled with sunshine. Sylvia spent hours planning and cooking, trying to make the meals full of nutriment. She was anxious that Gabriel should recover his strength completely. She did not want any of them to have regrets later. They were all so friendly that they dined with their guests in the communal dining-room as it saved Sylvia much running about, and she did not have two meals to prepare.

"Don't overdo it," Jeremy warned. "I know how you feel, but they'll get along now. I don't want you to get over-tired." He himself was busy from dawn until dark every day. Their own fresh vegetables appeared at the table daily, their own fruit, too, was ripening, and served up in some appetising dish for each meal. Sylvia enjoyed picking the fruit, and the children would often join her, their cans slung about their waists to leave their busy, destructive little hands free. They ate as much as went into the cans, she thought. They grew fairly expert in handling the bushes, and so long as they had not to stay too long at any one job, they were carelessly happy. They had remarkably little staying power, she found, studying them. Their chatter was entertaining as they moved slowly along the rows, keeping together by some means known among them, so that they could hear what was said. Sylvia discovered that she had a lively imagination and the children would keep silent for an hour if her stories could have lasted so long.

"I wish we'd scores more bushes," Jeremy said one day, watching them for a few minutes as they were all having a drink of lemonade by the red currants. "I'll plan for more next year. Don't stick at it too long, Sylvia. Take it as it comes. Dan will finish this lot tonight."

He never liked to see her working, she thought. The children came and went irregularly, as the mood took them. Jeremy had adapted one of the sheds for the use of the fruit, and it was always packed there either by himself or Dan, for the market. Sometimes it was stored until it could be used. Sylvia tried bottling as an experiment and was so delighted with the results that she continued.

Dan would bring in a bucket of fresh berries and slam them down near the kitchen table. His habit of dropping everything he held had to be restrained or the berries would have spilled on to the floor. He often stayed to help Sylvia pick the fruit and clean it before the bottling process began.

It was Dan who gave her several tips for making the jam set, and she began to revel in the sweet smell of boiling fruit. Her sugar bills grew formidable, and she wondered if they would be able to eat all she was making. The children adored jam and would have it with every meal if she allowed it. Every fresh boiling had to be sampled, but gradually, in spite of their large consumption, the jars on the shelves began to take up more and more room.

The one week lengthened into three while Gabriel recovered, and finally there was no talk of their leaving before the summer ended.

"We'll check in September," Janet said casually. "Why should we leave when it is doing Gabriel so much good? Don't you think he is gaining every day?" There was a challenge in her bright eyes. "There is no reason to count the cost if we can all stay together."

"He certainly does look stronger," Sylvia agreed. "It's strange and wonderful."

Jeremy and Gabriel often went fishing in the evening. Jeremy would take out the small boat and, although they did not apparently talk much on these outings, a lifelong friendship appeared to be developing between the two men.

Gabriel's thin, crooked back would be arched as he crouched over the side of the boat with the line in his sensitive fingers. He became expert, often catching more fish than Jeremy who had not his patience. What they brought in was always cooked for the next meal, and it tasted delicious, owing to its freshness. Gabriel began to complain that he was growing overweight but no one listened seriously. The chaffing was good to hear, Sylvia thought.

Dan shuffled his way through the weeks, occasionally dropping something that startled them all. In his own way he was happy, and he went down to the village only to collect their mail from the post office.

One evening Gabriel brought out his violin. It was not often that he played for an audience, and until now he had not seemed strong enough for the task. He was a shy man, conscious of his power over the instrument, and he feared to inflict anything on those with less feeling for the music. He appeared to need no score, for his memory was amazingly retentive.

Sylvia and Janet sat down on two of the chairs that were permanently out of doors. The children drifted towards them at the first low notes as their father tuned the instrument. Jeremy strolled forward, leaning against a tree smoking quietly. Dan sat on a tree stump with Bing at his feet. It was a peaceful scene.

Gabriel smiled as he saw them, and went from one lilting melody to another, playing what he thought would amuse and entertain. His thin fingers never tired as, with the violin tucked under his chin, he swayed to the nostalgia his music created.

He returned to Schubert persistently as if he liked it best of all.

The hours were like a miracle of time and space as the sadness gathered in the music of the trees and wind and lake. The sheen of the grass sloping down to the beach, the curve of a graceful bird in slow flight, all were picked up in that haunting, echoing beauty and flung on and on, so that one fancied it reverberated in all the far places of the world.

Sylvia grew still, her mind going down strange paths. Was this Gabriel's compensation for so much that he was missing from life? Was there always compensation if one sought for it? Yet Gabriel had so much—one only needed to see him with his family to know how much. She felt to be on the verge of some discovery and waited silently for the revelation.

Gabriel's playing of the classics showed faultless technique and there was nothing mechanical in his spirited rendering. He had a great love for Chopin's music, too, and returned more than once to the tone poems as if they haunted him. No one stirred as the night thickened about them and coolness touched their faces. They were drugged by the music his skill poured over them so prodigally.

Finally the light failed, and they all stirred when he ceased playing. Jeremy remained motionless, his foot against the tree, his pipe cold in his clenched hand. He had forgotten to smoke.

"One more, dear," Janet pleaded. "You know which one."

The rippling notes seemed a continuation of the silence into which she had spoken. Sylvia wondered what would be the favourite of so sophisticated a woman.

"Shall I sing?" Janet said.

They were all surprised anew, for it was hard to distinguish the human voice from the violin as Janet rose, pouring out her feeling in a burst of melody. Her voice was as strong and true and sweet as a nightingale's, whose song she sang.

Gabriel continued to the end, holding the quivering notes, and Janet ceased, looking about her abstractedly.

The silence was completely satisfactory. When she felt steadier Sylvia said: "That was a wonderful surprise . . . and very, very lovely."

Gabriel came to them, still holding the

violin as if afraid to put it down in the dim light. "Why don't you explain, my dear? My wife was a stage singer for many years. This last piece is still her favourite— although so difficult."

"Ah." It was Jeremy's voice, the children had trailed indoors with Dan. "That explains a lot. I must have seen your photograph years ago, for I felt to have known you somewhere."

"I was much photogaphed at one time. I used to love my stage work."

"She left the theatre to marry me," Gabriel prompted.

"Yes; we'd known each other for several years and it might have continued like that, just being friends, if I hadn't been involved in an accident when leaving the theatre one night. I realized that my career might be finished. Gabriel came often to see me, and . . ."

"I'd loved her for years," Gabriel's calm voice drifted out of the gloom. "I'd never have dared to tell her if she hadn't been ill."

"Our music first drew us together, but I'd never thought that he would ever be my husband," Janet said gently. "When he told me . . ."

"I took her to hear her understudy singing that piece she's just been singing now." Gabriel chuckled at the memory. "Half way through I managed to summon up courage to ask her to marry me. She said—' Yes, I'll marry you, but she shouldn't prolong that top note quite so long.'"

"If I did, it was sheer nerves," Janet was laughing, too. "He used to bring dozens of roses to the hospital and I had got the idea he liked me . . ."

"Yours is a real romance," Jeremy said.

"It doesn't always feel romantic when I'm coping with three small boys." Janet spoke cheerfully, for she adored her sons.

Jeremy struck a match to light his pipe, and the brief flare destroyed the intimacy that was growing between them.

Janet got to her feet again.

"We'd better go in now. Good night."

"Thank you for a very lovely experience," Sylvia said.

They had no unpleasant memories, she thought enviously. There was nothing now to spoil the perfection of what they shared.

Each was content in the other. She envied them their repose and content. She felt outside, harassed by her thoughts, for ever pulling against the shackles that seemed to bind her to the uneasy past. The thought stayed with her as she braced herself against the cabin door. She had been foolish to give herself time to think. Only in a busy life could she find the contentment which she sought. Janet had found an inner calm without which she could not have lived successfully. Janet had not the remorse of an unhappy marriage behind her.

How did one achieve the balanced day to day living that was necessary? How could one dispel the misery that memory brought? She went into the bedroom to brush her hair, anxious to be done with exhausting thought, but she had washed the brush and comb that morning, and they were in the kitchen where she had left them to dry.

Jeremy entered, watching her, holding his pipe thoughtfully.

"You—almost ran away, Sylvia."

"I." She wished he had not followed her, that he had given her time. How could she explain the confusion in her mind?

"I wish you and I could be as honest with each other as they are," he said.

"I am honest."

"Then what is it that comes between us?" he urged. "Just now—out there—I felt you draw away from me."

"Did I? I didn't realize. Perhaps you know why?"

He considered her words seriously. "No. Have I hurt you in any way?"

"No—and you imagine any difference," she said.

"Then why don't you answer my question?"

"You press me too far, Jeremy. I don't know why I feel this way sometimes. I get pushed into the past and start remembering, and something hurts me. I don't want it to hurt you, too. Forget about it —please."

He came to her, stopping her nervous movement with the hair brush. "Do I fail you in any way. Am I taking my share?"

She leaned against him tiredly. "Oh, Jeremy! Don't think this into something. It has nothing to do with our life together

—except that I can't forget what has gone. Never think that I'm unhappy with you. If I were not sure of your love I don't know what I'd do. Bear with me a little longer. One day I may be the woman Janet is."

"I don't want Janet," he told her, putting his arms about her. "It's you I want."

She knew that he was far from satisfied but he would not question her further. Her moods must bewilder him at times. Contritely she lifted her face for his kiss. She must try to reassure him. She laughed shakily, seeing the hairbrush still clutched in her hand.

"I look as if I meant to hit you with it, but I'm not as bad as that, am I?"

She felt relieved to have side-tracked the main issue successfully. She wondered if this delving into memory had stirred Janet or Gabriel in the same way? But their memories held only happiness—shared happiness—and that could not haunt their love.

The following morning Jeremy awoke with a plan in his mind. He spoke of it as he sat on the side of the bed, yawning before dressing. "You're doing too much."

"I'll admit my back aches constantly," she told him. "Perhaps it is the constant physical reminder of that fall down the stairs, that will not let memory rest." She was determined to be as frank with him as she could. "I'm never free of it."

"We must get someone to help you with the cooking and so on. I'm not having you standing at a stove any longer. I can't see any sense in killing you with work."

"It would be rather nice if someone took the responsibility off me." Her dark eyes brightened at the thought. "I would like that. Can we afford it this first summer? How do we get someone?"

"We can afford it and I believe Dan knows someone in the district who might come. I'll see about it today." He yawned again and stretched out one foot to draw his shoes closer.

She laughed shakily. "I'm just low spirited. Do forgive me, Jeremy."

"I can forgive you anything," he agreed, leaning back to kiss her, "except your being unhappy with me. I won't have that, darling."

They were happier than for some days, and she realized that he had noticed her depression although she had tried to hide it from him.

When Dan was approached about finding some help he said he knew just the person for the job if she were free.

"But she's mighty popular," he warned thoughtfully.

"Let's hope she's free, or soon will be," Jeremy said briskly. "I'll go down now and interview her."

Three hours later he arrived back with Kate in the car. Sylvia felt a little blank with the suddenness of it all. Kate carried a small suitcase, while Jeremy strode after her with a very heavy one. Obviously she had come prepared to stay indefinitely. He was grinning good-naturedly, and said mildly that he'd enjoyed his morning.

"Kate *was* free and she said she'd come right away. It took her exactly ten minutes to pack, ten to settle her affairs, and here we are. She's quite a woman."

Kate looked around fifty, dark with something gipsyish about her fresh features. Hair and eyes were brown, and she glowed with health, having an amazing energy in spite of her bulk.

She greeted Dan coldly. "So it was you. I thought as much—and much good will it do you, too."

Dan looked sheepish. Her sudden appearance confused him for he had not prepared any answers. He whistled for Bing and walked away, muttering under his breath. Kate sniffed with vigour. It was a habit to which they soon became accustomed.

Sylvia smiled at the by-play, not understanding. "I'll show you to your room. Jeremy, would you put the bags in there, please?"

Kate was to sleep in one of the cabins, an arrangement she approved. "I only sleep six hours out of the twenty-four," she confided. "I like privacy so that I can read when I feel like it. I'm a great reader. I'm on Thackeray at the moment, but I don't know about him, somehow. Ah! You've a little stove in here, too. I can make myself a cup of coffee when I need one. Now this is pretty nice. I'll stay. I can unpack later. What else is there to see? I've never been up here before."

Sylvia took her to see the other cabins, finishing up in the dining-room and kitchen where Kate would reign in future. She approved the arrangements there also, purring with pleasure when she saw the new equipment. Life would run smoothly where Kate was happy, Sylvia thought, and might come close to disaster if she were not. Her presence was too large not to make itself felt.

Kate filled the kettle and set it on the stove to heat. "I'll see about a cup of tea at once. Mr. Lang explained about things as we came up."

"Yes—tea at four; supper usually about six-thirty. We have something cooked for supper. You'll meet the guests when they come up from the beach. When they don't return for tea I usually make a picnic and take it down to them."

"Then you spoil 'em," Kate snapped. "Folks should know the rules."

"They are here in search of health, and we're anxious to do what we can." Sylvia told her as much as she thought advisable about Gabriel and his wife and family.

Kate's sympathy was gained as she listened. "Ah, that's different. That sure is a pity."

"You'll forget his disability the first time you talk to him," Sylvia prophesied. "I'll put the china in the basket."

"Sandwiches?" Kate demanded with an economy of words that seemed habitual to her. "These little cakes? Cookies? Scones?" She was looking in tins as she spoke.

Sylvia nodded. "What sort of filling for the sandwiches today? Any ideas?"

Kate had several, and the basket she presently carried down to the beach was well filled with appetising dainties. She approached the little group, who clustered together while Gabriel read aloud. He stopped when they heard her, and rose to his feet. His three sons followed suit, and Kate coloured deeply with sudden pleasure. She waved a brown hand to them energetically.

"That sure is nice of you folks—but please sit. I've brought your tea. I'm the new help—come to help Mrs. Lang with the cooking. How do you like this place?"

Janet answered her, for the male

element appeared tongue-tied. "We all like it very much, thank you."

"I think I will, too. I live in Locker but I've never been here before." Her face darkened and she looked as if she would have liked to add to the information but desisted. She spread the spotless cloth, weighting it with stones, and Gabriel helped her to distribute the parcels of food.

Charles, Pat and Tony were already taking their places, their eyes on the eatables. Kate produced the huge teapot, still piping hot. The load she had carried had been considerable but she had scarcely felt it. Jeremy always helped Sylvia when they picnicked.

"Supper will be ready at six-thirty sharp —and don't be late. I don't like what I cook to be kept waiting." She smiled at them in a friendly way to show there was no ill feeling before going back up the slope. Kate never stood on ceremony and she liked to know with what she had to reckon from the outset. Gabriel smiled at his wife and for some minutes they were busy attending to the wants of their family.

"I like her," he said finally, reaching for another sandwich.

"So do I. Oh, isn't everything perfect? We've not had rain once since we came."

"Jeremy says there's danger of a forest fire," Charles heard them. "He says it might rain tonight, too, so that would be good, wouldn't it?"

"I expect so," Janet agreed, looking across to the scarred acres on the other side of the lake.

"Now . . ." Pat said when they finished the meal. "Let's hear the rest of the story, Daddy. You'd got to the bit about the tubes boring into the earth's core . . ."

Sylvia soon found that Kate's presence made a considerable difference to her. There was now no pressure in preparing the meals. Kate stood firmly between her and so much that had seemed harassing. Kate appeared to have the strength of a man and she never complained of feeling tired. When she had finished the supper and washed up, she would retire to her cabin and would not be seen again until next day.

Occasionally, when Gabriel played his

violin for their entertainment, Kate would join the group, knitting a cardigan, for she was never idle.

She was not on speaking terms with Dan, or else her conversations were conducted in privacy. At some time in his career Dan must have trangressed beyond Kate's short patience, and she had no further use for him. She would put his plate in front of him and leave it at that. What he put on it was his affair. Dan accepted her lack of interest meekly, until Sylvia began to wonder.

A letter arrived for Jeremy from England, with news that his stepmother, Deborah and his brother, intended to visit them the following year. Almost every week letters passed between them, but this was the first intimation Jeremy had received that his family would join him.

"We'll certainly have plenty to show them," he told Sylvia thoughtfully. "You'll be glad to have them, too, won't you?"

"Yes. I love Deborah; her kindness to me I can never forget. I like your brother, too. How will he manage to get leave from

130

the Bank? He's not been abroad before, has he?"

Jeremy was still reading the letter. "He's doing without a holiday this summer and doubling up next year. I hope it works out for him. They should be able to spare us at least a month."

"Oh, it will be wonderful. Jeremy, we're building a home, aren't we?" She leaned against his shoulder contentedly.

"We sure are. I'm glad you're settling down at last."

Sylvia felt that life was shaping itself into a pattern, and the pattern was to her taste. "I'm having a wonderful time. In fact I'm in danger of relaxing too far. Kate is a treasure. Oh, Jeremy, I love you." She leaned close and hugged him round the neck. Jeremy looked up, flushing, for the embrace pleased him.

Kate appeared in the doorway, eyeing them truculently. "Sorry—but the kettle's leaking. I banged it on the stove yesterday —that did it. Have you another?"

Sylvia went to find the one they kept for their own use. Kate followed her, still grumbling. "Dan can mend kettles. You'd best tell him to get on with it, hadn't you?"

"Yes, I will, Kate. He seems to be able to do most things. Will this do for the moment?"

Later, when Dan came in from the garden with Bing trailing at his heels, Sylvia mentioned the leaking kettle to him. He looked thoughtful and was so long answering that she wondered if he meant to refuse to repair it for Kate. He dropped the heavy spade he was carrying, making her jump, although Sylvia knew it was one of his peculiarities to drop everything he held. It left his hands and landed where it would.

"I'll see to it," he promised "Aye . . . after supper, like . . ."

For some reason he spruced himself up for the evening meal, appearing with his hair wet and close to his head. Kate sniffed audibly, but she got up and brought his plate which had been keeping warm on the stove. The tureens of food were still hot, although distributed about the tables.

From Gabriel's table came an unceasing flow of conversation, as Janet tried to answer the numerous questions fired at her. Gabriel often had spells of dreamy silence for he lived in a world apart.

Dan reached for the food and gave himself large helpings of everything but the spinach.

"Anything wrong with the spinach?" Kate demanded tartly. It was not often she addressed him, and they all looked up.

"No, I just don't like spinach, that's all, Kate."

She sniffed significantly but did not press the point.

"This spinach has lots of butter in it, and eggs on top," Jeremy said slyly. "I never liked it either until Kate cooked it."

"There." Kate looked triumphantly at Dan, who was imperturbably eating what was on his plate.

"I don't like spinach—never did."

"You would like this spinach, Dan," Tony called from the adjoining table, and the two other boys joined in the refrain. "You would like *this* spinach, Dan . . . Dan . . . Dan." They beat time to the refrain with their forks and everyone laughed.

Dan did not reach for the spinach and

Kate's firm mouth hardened. "I don't like spinach," he spoke obstinately.

After the meal Sylvia stayed to help to clear away, but Kate would not allow her.

"I'm that mad . . . you get along now. Dan can lend me a hand—when he's finished *that* kettle."

"Sure, I'll help," Dan's horny hands reached for the dish towel.

Sylvia left them and went straight to Jeremy. "I wonder sometimes about Kate; now I'm wondering about Dan, too," she said.

Jeremy grinned. "Haven't you guessed? That warfare is only to hide their true feelings. Kate likes him but he's done something that made her mad and she's not an easy woman to cross. Like now over the spinach. I'll bet he eats spinach before she is through with him or his life will be a misery."

They laughed together as they went for their evening walk. The beach was quiet, the mountains close and sombre their heads lost in cloud. They could hear Janet putting her children to bed. Their happy, careless laughter and her gentle chiding came to them clearly down the slope. The atmosphere was clear and the air so still that all sounds were magnified. The cabin sounded like a nest of chirruping birds.

"I hope we'll have some like them—one day," Jeremy said.

"Yes." The smell of the small cigars that Gabriel smoked drifted down to them and Jeremy felt for his pipe as if reminded. "Oh, isn't the evening exquisite? The smell of tobacco, the sounds, the lush grass, the feeling that we're together—it's our life."

They walked close to the lake. It was cooler here, and the moment was so tremulous and revealing that they hesitated to speak. Almost before they knew it, it was gone, something that could not be recaptured. It was as if they had stepped back in time, through many centuries, to the dawn of the world. They were free as the air they breathed, without past or present—only the future with its beckoning fragrance. Jeremy stood silent, and Sylvia wondered if he experienced something of her ecstasy.

We have to live through humdrum hours to experience one moment of richness, she thought. Everything at this moment is clear. I love Jeremy and he loves me, and nothing else matters.

Jeremy caught her thoughtful, wistful look, and they smiled at one another. Without a word they turned away and began the ascent to the cabin.

During the following weeks Kate took most of the household management into her capable hands. She issued orders like a general on the eve of battle, revelling in her own prowess. Even Gabriel did her bidding, for he found that when Kate was pleased she was incredibly kind to his family. Janet openly admitted that she was trying to coax Kate away when they moved back to the coast.

Sylvia was amused. "You could ask her, but I doubt if she'll go. She is not the type to settle to ordinary domesticity. She needs a bigger canvas than routine housework. I saw that at the start. Besides, she likes Dan . . ."

"Yes, but he must be many years older than she is—and half her size—not that it matters, I suppose." Janet sounded exasperated.

"Nothing matters now that he has

mended her kettle. She lets him sit in the kitchen sometimes in the evenings."

"He still doesn't touch spinach though —and we seem to have plenty of it," Janet answered triumphantly.

Dan had a streak of obstinacy and Kate had found it, probably not for the first time. She was determined to break it down before they came to an understanding. Dan was equally determined that she would not. The battle was a silent one but entertaining to the watchers.

Fortunately the weather stayed exceptionally warm and fine. Sometimes when Sylvia wakened in the night she heard the sound of light rain pattering on the roof, but usually next morning there would be no trace, for the air was so hot that it dried moisture rapidly. It was on the very few rainy days that they were hard pressed to find occupation for the three children. One evening Janet ran across to the main cabin in her mackintosh. She shook it at the door and turned a despairing face towards Sylvia and Jeremy.

"SOS" She spoke laughingly. "*Can* you find something for my sons to do? We're hoarse from reading to them all afternoon.

137

We've run out of drawing paper and pencils and ideas generally. Gabriel is losing patience—he's been teaching them ju-jitsu! What to do? If only it were bedtime, but they refuse to go yet."

Jeremy grinned in sympathy. "How about a hand of Bridge?"

"They'd probably like it, but aren't they too young for that?"

Dan stirred in his corner by the fire where he had been waiting for the kettle to heat as he wanted to wash his feet. "How about a game of Snakes and Ladders—or Ludo? I've got the boards—carried them around with me for more 'n twenty years."

"It's years since I heard of those," Janet put her raincoat about her shoulders again. "May I bring them all over?"

While she was absent Dan produced his boards which were remarkably clean considering the length of time he had possessed them. He set them on the largest table in the room. Dice and 'tiddlywinks' as he called them, appeared from their sections of the same wooden box. It was evident that Dan at some time in his career had been forced into playing games of this nature. Sylvia found a large egg cup which acted as a dice box, as he appeared to have lost the original.

"We just used to roll 'em," he explained dryly. "Last time I had these out wez in the Yukon—way back. Me and me partner wez after gold . . . but we didn't never find none, no sir—not that trip."

"You must have had an exciting life," Sylvia suggested.

"Aye. Mebbe I'll tell you one day." His dry voice ceased when they heard the clamour of the children arriving. They were all draped in raincoats, which they shook carelessly as they removed them until the floor was dark with rain. Charles handed his coat to his father, but the others put theirs down on chairs, where Janet collected them with profuse apologies.

"What do we do?" Charles's colour came up with excitement when he saw the two boards. "What do we do, Dan? Is it like Inferno?"

"Nay, I never played Inferno." Dan explained the rudiments of each game while they listened politely. Sylvia, Jeremy and their parents stood prepared to watch.

The children felt that it was important and gave their whole attention to Dan.

"Tony is too young to play," Janet protested when the colours were sorted.

"He's not," Pat defended his brother. "Are you, Tony?"

"I'm not too young." Tony shook his head in violent negation, and rolled the dice out of the egg cup. A six turned up and Charles pounced on it.

"That means you're on, Tony. You can start first because you got a six. It's right for him to start first, Dan, because he's the youngest and if we don't tell him he won't know." Charles was shouting this information.

"Come on, Tony, roll it again," his mother urged, pleased with her youngest.

Tony rolled again and got one, which Charles moved on the board for him.

"I want to move my own," Tony shrieked, and put it back, and moved it forward again to show he could and would.

"If you quarrel you'll not be allowed to play," Gabriel said. Tony subsided.

It was Pat's turn with the dice and then Dan's, but neither could roll a six or get on to the board. Charles looked at them pityingly.

"You can't start without a six, can you?" He rolled another six and another and signified that he did not need any help in future.

It was funny how the game developed between Charles and his youngest brother. Neither of the other two players could even get on the board. The game narrowed into a twosome, and the onlookers felt the tension. Charles was a spirited boy, and one who fully realized the benefits that accrued to him by being the eldest of the family.

"Of course I'll win," he said with confidence. "Because I'm the eldest and Tony doesn't understand what we do unless we tell him."

But as quick as Charles rolled, Tony rolled one too, so that he followed Charles all round the board in an uncanny way.

"Just the luck of the game," Jeremy remarked, watching narrowly. They were all on their feet now, interested to see the outcome.

When Charles only needed three to make himself safe from further attack, he realized what Tony was doing. Jeremy went red in the face with suppressed laughter.

"Why—" Charles spoke indignantly. "He's trying to knock me off. Mother—look . . ."

Tony nodded placidly, one arm supporting his bright head as he lounged against the table. "Yes, I'll knock you off. Dan said I could." He promptly rolled a three.

The uproar that ensued was the funniest thing that Sylvia had ever known. Charles was so volubly indignant and taken aback that they felt quite sorry for him.

"Mother—he knocked me off . . . and I'd got round . . ." He was crying angrily.

"He had to knock you off—if he could. It's in the game," she told him.

"There have to be rules. You'd have knocked him off, wouldn't you?" Gabriel said, trying to keep the two boys apart.

Charles shook his head, his anger dying. "No, I wouldn't. I'd have let him stay on. But I will next time. I'll knock everyone off."

"That's a stupid attitude," Janet spoke

coldly. "It wouldn't be a proper game if you did that."

"If you don't play properly you get handicapped," Dan put in mildly. He was quite puzzled at the general frenzy the game incited.

"What's handicapped?" Charles was red in the face.

Dan tried to explain, and added: "If you were a real sport about someone winning you'd shake hands and congratulate him. That's part of it, too."

Tony understood that and he dashed round the room, shaking hands with everyone present and beaming because he had won a game he simply did not understand. When he reached Charles they shook hands amiably, for neither felt secure enough to make an issue of the matter. Charles was too good-natured to bear malice, and after a further wrestle with the rules, they started again.

This time, no matter how cunningly he rolled, Tony could not get a six to enable him to get on the board, and after waiting patiently for several turns while the others were sailing ahead without him, he threw down the dice in disgust.

"Give me a six," he yelled, digging his fists into the sofa cushion. "Give me a six. I want a six. Dan . . ."

"We can't give you a six. You've got to earn it," Dan told him.

"Then I won't play." Tony's face was belligerent, and he threw the dice on the floor deliberately.

"I think he's too young." Janet defended him without energy.

"If he intends to play he must follow the game," Gabriel's face was a study. "Get down and pick up that dice, Tony. Otherwise leave the table and go to bed."

The child looked up, without pouting mouth, but stooped to obey his father. He recovered the dice, putting it back on the table, and staying down an instant longer to recover. Presently he resumed the game, and when he rolled a six there was a shout of triumph from his brothers. Even in the midst of their anger with each other they hung together, and saw that justice was done to each in turn.

As Sylvia watched she realized how each mismove and small matter of cheating was carefully cut out by Gabriel. "It's playing that counts," he kept shouting over the clamour. "It doesn't matter who wins. *Anyone* can win . . ."

They played so many games that eventually each won in turn. Just how Dan worked this without being detected, Sylvia was never sure. She looked at the old man with a new respect.

"I'm glad you won," Pat said generously to Dan as they shook hands. There was this epidemic of hand-shaking at the end of every game. "I'd not have liked you *not* to win when you lent us the boards."

"Er—thanks . . ." Dan responded. No one could determine the expression that crossed his leathery face. "My kettle's boiling and I want to wash my feet before supper."

"Wash them in here," Tony invited anticipatorily. "I want to see you."

"I'll get the dish," Charles offered. "I'd like to pull out your corn. You said you had one."

"I'm taking the kettle into my own room," Dan looked shocked.

"Besides, you have to put the boards away and pack the dice so that they'll be ready for next time—if there ever is a next time," Janet was exhausted.

The boys rushed to help her. "When can we play again?"

"The next wet night?" She glanced at Sylvia. "Can you stand it?"

"Hope it's wet tomorrow," Charles said, releasing their laughter.

"Hope it's not. It's my birthday tomorrow." Janet turned their thoughts. "Gabriel has promised me a trip and I've chosen a sentimental journey. We wondered if you and Jeremy would like to come with us, Sylvia. We're taking camping equipment and will stay some-where over-night. Might be fun—if fine."

"I'd love to come. Where?" Sylvia asked, smiling.

"As far north as we can get in roughly six or eight hours. That would give us a fairly good range."

"Nice idea," Jeremy agreed. "You might meet some Indians. You're in Indian country. Anyway, you could swim and fish and so on."

"We have two tents with us, and the children could sleep in the back of the car." Janet had evidently thought it out.

"I'll pack lots of food. Don't let me forget a frying pan, Jeremy."

Charles let out a war whoop of sheer joy, and his brother followed him round the room as they slid and crouched over the furniture like Indians on the war path. They whacked their thighs, and whooped madly until Janet put a stop to the madness.

"I'll go and talk to Kate now," Sylvia murmured. She braved the rain and went to where Kate was dishing up the supper. They discussed what would be necessary for the trip. "I'll call the others now, shall I? Dan was washing his feet."

"He must be learning sense at last then, for he always used to wash his feet *after* a meal, and I told him that was no good." Kate revealed her knowledge of Dan there, Sylvia thought, but she did not comment.

The following morning they left the ranch about ten o'clock. Everyone was excited at the prospect of the drive. Kate was pleased that she was to have a day free of cooking. The children were tumbling about in the rear of the car like young monkeys and it was not until after their first meal had been eaten out of doors that they settled down. Gabriel, who was driving, kept to the main road most of the time, only deviating when sure that the subsidiary road was a good one. His car was an expensive one. Janet was cool and assured and pleasant, and told Sylvia in an undertone that she was sure she could have driven quite as well as her husband.

The remark was meant to be overheard, and Gabriel smiled. Sylvia thought she had never seen a lovelier look on anyone's face than the one he wore when he glanced back at them both. Jeremy was sitting by the driver, talking occasionally. They realized that they were passing through a forest where the silence was oppressive.

Towards four o'clock Janet said: "This is it? Don't you agree? The loveliest place in the world."

"Looks like it." Gabriel stopped the car and turned to explain. "Janet swore she would recognize the *Rose Marie* country if she ever saw it. This may be it. We don't know, but it's certainly as beautiful as anything we could find. We've taken it slowly, too."

They were on the shore of a smaller, unnamed lake, that shone like a jewel in the sunshine. A short distance away was a small jetty, with a boat tied up. Janet pointed inland to a hut that seemed to have grown among the trees. Trees were everywhere, sloping down to the very edge of the road, only to start up again closer to the lake. When Gabriel stopped the engine the silence settled broodingly around them. No one had the energy to leave the car.

"We'll camp here," Janet sighed happily.

"I don't know anyone who enjoys anything with every part of her as you do," Gabriel said. "This certainly is grand."

Janet laughed and pushed open the car door. Her hand was arrested when Pat, the middle boy, said piercingly: "Mother, why has Daddy got a lump on his back?"

Gabriel shrank into his seat, not turning his head. Janet's response came so swiftly that Sylvia knew she had been waiting for this question for a long time.

"Didn't you know, Pat? When he was your age he had a bicycle and used to ride all over Vancouver, until one day an accident happened, and he was thrown off. Everyone thought he was dead but they

149

managed to get him to hospital—and when he came out again his backbone began to grow like it is now."

It was so practically and simply said, and the explanation was so complete that no one questioned it further. Pat, overcome when it was too late, with sudden bitter realization of what his question had meant, pushed his way blindly from the rear of the car and threw his arms about his father's shoulders. Tears were running down his face. Gabriel lifted him over the seat and sat with him across his knees.

"Daddy—I didn't know. I didn't remember until now that you had a bad back . . ."

They knew it was true; the child had questioned it as soon as he noticed it.

"Is that why we can't have bicycles?" Charles asked crisply.

"I don't want a bicycle now," Pat sobbed on his father's knee. His swift repentance for his indiscretion, was part of his father's own tolerance and gentleness. Neither would have hurt the other for anything, for their natures were similar. Janet looked through the window, not speaking.

"I'm going to buy you all bicycles," Gabriel said. "Only we'll see that you know all the rules of the road first. That was where I perished."

"Was it that?" His wife asked.

"Yes, it was probably my own fault; I was too young to know properly. If I'd obeyed the rules it might not have happened. Most things in life are one's own fault."

"Yes—and we pay before we know the reason why," she spoke sadly. "Well, shall we get out? Who will collect the twigs for a fire? We can't make tea without a fire."

Pat looked tearfully into his father's face before getting off his knee. There was no anger there and the child was reassured. His smile had all the quality of an April day. Sylvia patted his little clenched fist. What might have been an embarrassing moment had turned into a lesson none of them would forget.

The children raced off to collect twigs. They were behaving like cowboys as they brought their loads back to the base every few minutes. When the men unloaded the car the women unpacked the hampers. Jeremy took off his shoes and socks and waded into the lake to fill the kettle. Charles followed him.

"We're only wading, mother," Charles shrieked. "Jeremy says there's a monster as big as an eel in the lake so we can't go in for one hour."

Janet was amused. "Eels are not all that big, son." She was glad that they were not to swim immediately. Sylvia set a cloth in the shade of a great maple, and stacked the food on plates. When the kettle boiled, Jeremy brewed the tea and brought it to them.

"I'm thirsty." Pat leaned forward confidentially, sliding to his place.

Jeremy sat with a child leaning against each knee, for in Jeremy they enjoyed an active comradeship that was not possible with their own father. His strength and knowledge fascinated them. It was Jeremy who had given them their first fishing lesson, and who brought them struggling from the lake when they defied parental persuasion and would not come in to order after swimming. Jeremy was strong and they respected that strength.

It was amazing how the piles of food vanished as they all ate rapidly.

"After all, there *are* seven of us," Janet pointed out.

"I could stay here for ever," Charles said in a grown-up tone. "In fact, I would *like* to stay, because then I wouldn't have to go to school."

"But I don't feel there would be much future in that," Janet told him feelingly.

After tea the two tents were erected. There were sleeping bags for all, and as the night seemed to be fine and warm, they were all looking forward to the experience of sleeping out of doors. The tents appealed to the three boys.

"But as Sylvia and Jeremy are our guests they must use the tent," Janet explained. "You will be all right in the car."

When they had all finally settled down for the night, in the stillness and moon radiance that filled the earth, Sylvia felt a deep content she had never known before. Life could be what they made of it. Her mind enveloped all that had once hurt her, and she realized that the strong fingers out of the past were losing their grip. She stretched and sighed.

"Warm enough?" Jeremy put his arm over her.

"Yes. I was enjoying the feeling of being so close to the stars. I wonder why we don't camp out more often? Can you hear a leaf patter down on the roof occasionally?"

"It's nice enough in warm weather," Jeremy agreed sleepily. "I've been under canvas when we haven't had a dry stitch on us—when our clothes have been frozen to our bodies—when we couldn't shake our ground sheets clear of the mud . . . um . . ."

"These sleeping bags are warm and comfortable."

"Good equipment does help. It's always the same in life. If you have the money you can make yourself comfortable." He yawned again and was soon asleep.

Yes, comparisons for Jeremy brought other thoughts. Through the silent, dark hours that followed Sylvia slept lightly, aware that here was the happiness that was for ever evading her. She was sensitive to the low sounds that broke through to the new day, the cheeping of birds, the sound of water . . . she sat erect when she heard

Janet singing. Jeremy grinned as he leaned up beside her, one hand going through his tousled hair.

Janet had gone where her lovely voice would have most appeal. The lingering, vital quality of the words she sang came with peculiar, echoing emphasis. They listened with deepening pleasure until the ringing final words slid away into the morning mists.

"She sure is enjoying this," Jeremy said, laughing.

There was a clamour of sound when the children pelted out of the car, leaving their sleeping bags trailing behind them. They raced to escort their mother from the jetty on which she had been standing. As they came back they all joined in a rollicking chorus. Jeremy went to light the fire and fill the kettle. In half an hour there was a meal ready—bacon, eggs, brown and white bread, butter, marmalade, scones, coffee.

"I've never been wakened in a nicer way," Sylvia spoke appreciatively.

"Are the children musical?" Jeremy asked.

"I think so—except for Pat. He's no

leaning that way yet, but he may grow to it."

"It would be strange if they weren't musical with two such fine musicians in the family," Jeremy bowed to Janet as he spoke.

She was pleased and her colour deepened. "Thank you, Jeremy."

The morning passed swiftly, while they all played games to please the children. Jeremy was first favourite as he knew all the outdoor games. He had brought a football, and showed them all he could of the game. His patience was remarkable but he did not indulge them in any way.

Sylvia was limp with tiredness before they were due to break off for the midday meal. It was almost three o'clock when it was finished, and the children bargained for another swim before they must return to the ranch.

"All right," Janet agreed, "but not longer than twenty minutes in the water. I'll time you." Jeremy stalked off with the three boys, while Janet and Sylvia repacked the picnic hampers. Janet stood by what she had said and called to the bathers in the time she had stated.

Charles and Pat came obediently, but Jeremy had to carry a squirming Tony to the shore. He set him down wrathfully, not commenting.

"Tony wanted to swim to China," Pat gave it away to his parents as they dressed. "Jeremy wouldn't let him."

"I should think not." Janet frowned at her youngest. "China, indeed! Whoever heard of such a thing—when I said you were to return in twenty minutes."

"Oh, I wouldn't have been as long as that," Tony said, looking depressed. He was in disgrace for a while, but they all liked him too well to keep him that way, and he quickly forgot about it when they entered the car.

Sylvia thought the return journey was almost more pleasant than the outer one had been. Jeremy was driving now and she sat beside him. He was a careful and steady driver but he kept the speed of the car up because they were late in starting and Janet had said she wished to get the children home before dark. Jeremy took no risks but he did take advantage of the fact that there was practically no traffic on the road. Sylvia knew he was enjoying the valuable car, for he had not had the chance to drive it before.

"That was a splendid run," Janet said when they stopped at the ranch. "Thank you."

"I'm going to be a chauffeur when I grow up," Pat said, sleepily. "Mother, can we have ginger ale before we go to bed?"

"No, dear. Milk would be best tonight." Janet sorted her brood who waited in the dusk.

Kate came towards them, with Bing bounding beside her.

"You folks got back safely. I sure am glad. I'll take some of that stuff." Kate never said more or less than she meant.

"Where's Dan?" Jeremy asked.

"I wouldn't know," Kate told him, adding truthfully, "but I wouldn't be surprised if he comes home roaring drunk."

They heard Gabriel chuckle somewhere in the car. Charles grumbled because he thought he could smell cockles, and his mother assured him that he must be mistaken.

"What strange fancies children have at night," Janet spoke fretfully.

"You can all have your suppers in bed," Gabriel settled the many arguments that appeared to be starting. "We'll bring you each a tray."

Kate nodded and went off to see the order was carried out, convinced that she only liked children in small doses. Supper in bed meant more freedom for her to hear about the trip.

Later that night, Sylvia heard Dan returning from the village. "He doesn't sound to be drunk, does he, Jeremy?"

"He's not the sort to show it if he is," Jeremy grunted.

"I wonder if he and Kate quarrelled?"

"They're a couple of queer cards. I can't think what we're doing with them both around, either." The thought made them laugh so much that sleep fled.

"' Some people are born great—others have greatness thrust upon them,'" Sylvia misquoted. "Oh, Jeremy, I've enjoyed these two days."

"So have I, darling. We'll do it again some time, eh?"

Although Kate's words had made them all curious no one could guess from Dan's dry demeanour the following day whether or not he had returned in an inebriated condition. He was about at his usual early hour, filling the wood boxes for Kate, and doing his usual chores.

"But I smelled his breath," Charles told his astonished mother. "It smelled of that stuff Daddy takes when he has a cold."

"Does it, indeed?" Janet was shocked, for she had not been aware that Kate's remark had been overheard by her brood. "Then probably Dan has a cold, too. I wouldn't be surprised either, for the frost around him would give anyone a chill."

This amused Gabriel so much that he was unable to explain to the perplexed child what she meant. Charles wandered outside to look for Jeremy and a game of cricket.

Tony, not yet five years of age, had an inquisitive mind. When Kate was preparing supper that night, growing hot and cross under the pressure that evolved at such a time, he put his head round the kitchen door, smiling sweetly.

"Hullo, Kate. What are we having?"

"Baked fish," she answered shortly, for it was not the half of it, she thought.

He stood on one leg, his head on one side, considering her. "Where is your husband, Kate?"

Kate lifted a pan lid and pretended to look under it. "He's not here."

Tony suspected that she was not treating the matter seriously as she began to glance in the cupboards, keeping her head turned away. "Haven't you got one?"

"Why? Should I have one?" Her voice was hard.

"Everybody needs a husband." He pointed out logically: "Mother has one, Sylvia has one. Haven't you one?"

"No, I haven't." Kate was fast losing patience in the persistent questioning. "Where would I keep a husband?"

"Oh, you don't 'keep' them anywhere," he pointed out. "They are just around— like Daddy."

"Yes, but you have to feed 'em." Kate added salt to the potatoes and realized it was the second time she had done this. She scowled into them darkly.

"Oh, not always. Sometimes they feed themselves. Kate . . ."

"Well?"

"Wouldn't Dan do?"

161

She spun round on the small boy, making him blink. "What do you mean?"

"For a husband."

"No, he wouldn't." She looked about her for something on which to lay her hands and the frying pan happened to be nearest. With this in hand she chased Tony out of the kitchen and for some distance. "Just you keep out of my way . . ."

Tony almost ran into Jeremy who was returning from cleaning out the pigs. "What have you been up to this time, Tony?"

"You keep quiet," Kate warned in a terrible voice.

Tony shook his head and twisted out of Jeremy's grasp. He ran off without divulging the source of the quarrel. Kate dropped the empty frying pan to arm's length and began to chuckle.

"Those children will be the death of me. Keep them out of my kitchen if you want me to do any more cooking," she warned.

Jeremy promised to cooperate and went on to the main cabin. He told Sylvia what had occurred but it was not until the children were going to bed that they heard Tony's version of what had happened.

"He's right," Janet defended him, "but he must not annoy Kate. I'll try to make him understand—but it's difficult."

Tony had his own brand of diplomacy and went to work speedily. The next day he presented himself to Kate with two buttons off his miniature shirt.

"I'm miserable when I haven't got my buttons shut, Kate." He spoke plaintively.

"Of course you are, poor lamb. I'll sew them on for you. Where's your ma? Can't she sew?"

"Yes, but she's busy washing." Tony smiled enchantingly as he handed over the two buttons. He watched with interest while Kate made an excellent job of sewing them on. When she finished he kissed her gravely on both cheeks. "Thank you, dear Kate. I like you. If you want I'll be your husband when I grow up."

"Well, for the love of Pete!" Kate wailed in exasperation. "Can't you forget it?"

Tony shook his head and she noticed that he edged to the door for safety's sake.

"No. I want you to have one if everyone has one . . ."

She could see fairness in the remark, and inwardly agreed with him although she would have died sooner than admit it.

"Good morning, Tony." Her voice was grim.

"Good morning, Kate." He nodded and ran out, convinced that he had been nice to Kate as his mother had wished him to be.

4

SYLVIA'S illness came on so quickly that everyone was surprised. The ambulance called and took her to the nearest hospital, where she was detained for two weeks.

"The actual trouble is a badly sprained back—relic of that awful fall," she wrote to Jeremy. "It has ached for months but I didn't want to keep complaining. It isn't very serious, so don't worry, darling. Soon be home again . . ."

She needed the enforced rest so much that she almost enjoyed the time in hospital. Her low spirits had sprung from a physical cause, which she recognized and finally routed. Jeremy called at the hospital to take her back to the ranch, and they were shy with each other. He was tender in his care of her as he helped her into Gabriel's big car, borrowed for the occasion.

"I mustn't hurt you. The nurse has been

laying down rules left, right and centre. You've to rest for several weeks yet."

"I'm all right. I feel wonderful," she told him. "You look well, Jeremy."

"I am. Partly Kate's cooking. She blames herself for your illness—says you must have swallowed something that disagreed with you."

"Oh, if only that were so. No, this has been coming on for ages—I'll tell her."

Jeremy gave her such items of news as he thought would interest her, as he started the big car and drove along the lake shore. "We've had three lots of guests— one week-end we were so busy I felt like throwing it all up and going fishing. Kate —restrained me."

"Who came?"

"A young couple for the week-end . . . said they'd come again. Then someone Janet knew—a relative of theirs I think. Christine . . . she stayed a week. They took her out with them. I went along a couple of times."

Sylvia felt curious about Christine. "What's she like?"

"She is an artist—paints anything. Quite good too, some of the stuff."

"I wish I'd been at home," Sylvia said.

"The kids have been little devils . . . don't tell Janet but I could have chucked them all in the lake. Every time I got in a mess I realized we had you to thank for the smooth working of everything . . . Kate included."

She flushed warmly, and put her hand under his arm. "Thank you, Jeremy."

"Kate's all right but too bossy for me. She orders us about as if we haven't minds of our own." He laughed grimly. "She was downright rude to Christine; it was probably why she left earlier than she intended. She may come later on, though."

Sylvia knew how irksome any restraint was to Jeremy. "Well, it's over for you, dear. You can get back to your gardening and the bees and the pigs and the apples and things. They'll all come again—the guests I mean, so don't worry about Kate."

"Kate's policy . . ." he began hotly, his fair brows knitting. "If it had anything to do with me I'd like to have our good Kate where I could put her right on a few matters. She forgets herself at times. You might drop her a hint, darling." Jeremy sounded ruffled.

"Don't worry about her. I'll take care of Kate. She means well—fortunately."

"By the way, Gabriel has booked their two cabins again for next summer."

"Oh—marvellous," Sylvia's eyes were shining. "Isn't it remarkable that all this has risen out of a casual meeting in a café in Vancouver? He's better, too . . ."

The car was passing through a long, shaded glade, part of the road that followed the edge of the lake for miles, weaving along the base of the mountain like a centipede. Jeremy stopped the car, pulling in to the side. He put one arm round Sylvia's shoulders, and with the other covered her clasped hands.

"Darling, I've missed you—like nobody's business, and I love you fit to beat the band. Glad to be coming home to me?"

She smiled reassuringly into his eyes, turning her hands in his gently. "Terribly glad. I've missed you, too. Oh, darling . . ."

He kissed her full on the mouth, before they drove on.

Sylvia was quickly drawn back into the busy life she had learned to enjoy. It was September now, the days closing in, the wood fires smelling delightfully of the autumn. Gabriel and Janet decided that the time had come to return to the coast, and their children cried openly as they collected their treasures from every part of the ranch. Bats, balls, toys, games, ropes, so completely had they made themselves at home that it took a couple of days to pack them back into the big car.

"If we forget anything you could keep it till next year," Charles said. They would have taken Dan's Ludo board had their mother allowed it, but she hastily promised to buy them one of their own in Vancouver. They also wished to take Bing with them, but Bing had other ideas. Dan pretended to coax the dog to follow the children, but his allegiance was never in doubt.

Kate's dark face was a battleground as she waited to see them off. She was never definitely sure that she liked children, but these had such endearing qualities that they had gained her good will and she knew it would be lonely without them. She thought of the extra work they had brought her, but none of it counted against the total of their love for her as they pressed warm kisses against her brown cheek, and almost strangled her with the weight of their arms about her neck.

Janet came to where Sylvia was standing watching the car being loaded.

"Well—our meeting that day must have been ordained, Sylvia. It brought us a lot of happiness." Their glances met, and they smiled seriously. Their first liking for each other had deepened until they felt like sisters. "Gabriel is driving us home . . ." Her face shone when she recalled his promise. At the time they had all doubted his ability, but Gabriel was strong again. "We've been with you nearly four months."

"You must often have felt bored," Sylvia suggested.

"Never." Janet spoke cheerfully.

Kate heard the remark and sniffed audibly. No one need be bored if they had Janet's money, for every week a dozen magazines and several books had come for her through the mail; she had gone to town whenever she needed her hair shampooing or to shop for herself and the children. Kate's sniff signified her contempt for these amenities, and Janet laughed understandingly. She had Kate's measure and would as gladly have taken her to town as her sons wanted to take Dan's Ludo board.

At last they had to go. Jeremy checked the tyres for the last time. Gabriel shut the door decisively on his small brood. The children waved, silent now, their expressions regretful. The long car pulled into the lane, and the horn sounded a prolonged blast that continued until they were out of sight.

"Well—that's over." Sylvia took Jeremy's arm as they strolled towards the cabins that had just been vacated. It was silent and lonely without their guests.

"I wonder if you'll like it quite so well now it's quiet again," Jeremy said.

"Somehow this is where our *real* life begins," she spoke contentedly. "Our first winter together. Yes, I'll like it."

For a few days Sylvia and Kate were busy washing sheets and blankets and slips, sorting, putting away, and generally tidying, ready for the next year. The cabins had to be thoroughly cleaned and colour-washed again to freshen them, carpets were rolled up and lifted from the floors so that they would not gather damp. Soon all was safe against the coming winter storms.

"And what about me?" Kate demanded when there was nothing more to do.

It was now October and the Kootenays were glowing golden brown in their autumn beauty. Wherever the eye lighted that sienna tint was in evidence, storing beneath its crispness the promise of another spring. Sylvia could scarcely bear to remain indoors.

"Do you want to stay or would you prefer to go to Nelson for the winter?" she asked Kate. "We can't afford to pay you much when there are no guests but . . ."

"The money won't matter if I can stay rent free," Kate clinched matters in her usual forthright way. "I could stay in my own cabin for it's not exposed as some of the others. I'll be fine there all winter."

"I'll see Mr. Lang about it and let you know," Sylvia spoke with dignity. She knew that Jeremy would be influenced by her own wish in the matter.

"She'd be company for you," Jeremy said. "I don't want you to overdo things again so take all the rest you can."

Kate was pleased with the arrangement and settled in. Every morning she appeared to cook breakfast then she would wash up, tidy the main cabin, and cook the midday meal. She would then disappear for the rest of the day, sometimes to go visiting in the neighbourhood, or if the weather was bad, to read or knit or listen to the radio in her comfortable cabin.

Sylvia felt that she must often feel lonely, and made tentative inquiries.

"I'm never lonely," Kate told her. "I've always wanted time to think and to be by myself like this. Until now I've always been at somebody's call, always had to consider what someone else wanted. Now I don't, and you've no idea how I appreciate it. My life has been so full and so busy that I've not been able to live it properly. Does that sound odd?"

"A little, but it's one's outlook that counts. I'd have thought you would miss all the life and bustle."

"No. I'm just thankful it's over for me. I enjoy what I have now."

"If you *do* want company at any time, come over and sit with us." Sylvia did not like to feel that anyone connected with her might be lonely.

"It's not likely. I knit and think, or read. I'm catching up with that at last."

There was a twinkle in Sylvia's dark eyes. "Have we found the contented woman at last? You don't appear to have a single want."

"Oh, I'll be through with it come spring. It's because I know there will be an end to it that I'm enjoying it so completely." Kate laughed her jolly laugh. "I wonder if that Christine will come again in the spring."

"Why do you say that?" Sylvia hesitated by the door.

"She wants to get married does that one," Kate's voice was sarcastic. "I don't think much of her, and that's a fact."

"Well, I expect she'll come if she said she would. Doesn't she paint? What's she like?"

"Pretty—too pretty . . ." Kate said, grudgingly.

"What's wrong with that?"

"Nothing—if they use it the right way."

Sylvia let the matter drop, knowing that Kate had drawn her own conclusions about Christine. Nothing Sylvia could say would alter the older woman's mind, for she had not yet met Christine.

It was a gusty day, wind blowing hard against the trees, so that the cabin was surrounded by a sea of sound. Sylvia loved that increasing roar, when it felt as if the sea knocked unceasingly against their door. At night she would lie awake, luxuriating in the warmth of the blankets, vibrantly alive to the movements in the vast outdoors. Storms came, the rain beat down, the days grew steadily colder. The cabin was storm-proof and, although the rain sometimes spluttered down the chimney, there was never any danger from the intense cold. Dan kept the woodpile high and the two stoves were kept going all day.

"Just remember to wrap up warmly whenever you go out of doors," Jeremy warned her. "A few minutes in this low atmosphere is enough to give you a chill, so don't forget."

The days sped so quietly, and so happily, that Sylvia was genuinely surprised one day to see that the calendar pointed to the end of January. The winter was almost over. Snow covered the ground, ice lay on the lake edge in places.

One morning they rose early, tempted out, by the sunshine, into their white crisp world.

"I'd like to skate if the ice is thick enough at Banana Bay," Jeremy's breath curled out in front of his mouth as they hurried into thick coats and mufflers.

"Oh, no, Jeremy." She stopped uncertainly. "I'm sorry, dear, I know you hate me to say no to anything, but sometimes I feel I can't bear it when you go swimming or skating alone—anything that may be dangerous." She tried to laugh, knowing he did not relish a too-tight rein.

"You're in love." He bent to kiss her cold cheek.

"Yes, but it's more than that. I remember my feeling of premonition the day I thought you were drowned. Come on, let's keep moving or we'll chill." They walked through the crisp air, almost cleaving through it, for the frost was hard against them. They were young and strong and could not keep to a sober pace.

"One thing about this district—you know exactly where you're going every time you turn out because you've only two roads to choose from," Jeremy said.

"Nor's and sou's . . ." Sylvia laughed as he raised an eyebrow. "I heard someone describe it like that once in Switzerland. She spoke excellent English but could never put over the Nor's and Sou's properly."

"You never told me you'd been to Switzerland." There was sudden tension in his voice. "Morgan take you?"

"No. I went with my mother when I was about eighteen. Hadn't I told you? We went to Paris, too, and before that to Italy. My mother loved travelling." She sensed that the feeling in him died under her explanation. There was never any tension between them save when Morgan was remembered. A chill came across the brightness of the morning and some of the joy died out of her. She began to feel like a meal.

"Let's see if Kate has breakfast ready yet. We've a mile to walk back . . ."

They could smell the bacon and hot cakes down on the road, for the atmosphere was so low that the air eddied with the weight of the odour. It whetted their keen appetites. All four sat down to an excellent meal. Jeremy and Dan discussed the proposed skating, but Sylvia could not muster any enthusiasm.

"Isn't it dangerous?" she asked the old man.

"Oh, it's safe enough at Banana Bay," the old man said, and then caught Kate's warning glance. "Wal . . . sometimes there is an accident . . . once . . ."

"Once is enough," Kate passed him the bacon dish which he loved to mop up with dry bread. "I'm baking this morning so you'd best all keep out of my way."

Sylvia wondered what Jeremy would do, for she knew that before she joined him he had skated many times during the previous winter. She helped Kate with the washing-up.

"I'd feed the brute," Kate said slowly, while she was turning the bread tins in the oven. "Most men don't bother to turn out when they are well fed. What's his favourite dish—if he has one?"

Sylvia was startled, and knew her thoughts had been read. "He likes tomato soup, corned beef and cabbage—done in big lumps, you know—and lemon pie . . ." she spoke hopefully, wondering if they could manage all that.

"If he ain't sick it won't be our fault, eh?"

They set to work to convert the wish into a meal. Jeremy showed his appreciation at noon. The tomato soup was creamy and seasoned to his taste. Kate pressed a second helping on both men. The corned beef and cabbage came to the table in the baking bowl for there was nothing else large enough to hold it. The cabbage was quartered, frosted, cooked to delicate perfection, and melted on the fork.

Jeremy sat back replete, for both men found it a filling dish. "I couldn't eat another thing."

Sylvia popped the lemon pie in front of him. With its high meringue, skilfully browned to the exact shade demanded in the cookery books, it was a pleasant sight.

"Well—I might just manage one piece . . ." Kate saw to it that the lemon-pie found its way to the right plates. Dan dared not refuse his after the look she gave him. Coffee followed, topping an enormous meal. "What is this—a conspiracy? I've never eaten so much at a sitting since I was in my 'teens. Are you two women trying to put something over on me? Putting up my weight—or killing my skating ambitions?"

They knew themselves discovered and they all laughed. The smell of the baking bread hung pleasantly around the cabin. Jeremy settled down to read, and in a few minutes his fair head leaned back against his chair and he was asleep. Kate tiptoed away.

"I'll see you for supper," she hissed, waving Dan in front of her.

Sylvia sat down opposite Jeremy, content as she had not been all day. The warmth of the baking was behind them, the heaviness of the afternoon shut out and she had Jeremy safe. She looked at him, seeing the handsome fairness of his head. He had kicked off his boots before the meal and was in slippers. There was a

180

helplessness about him in sleep that would be dispelled the moment he awoke.

This is much better than him being alone at Banana Bay . . .

Jeremy awoke, and smiled across at her. "I felt you watching me. You didn't want me to go skating, did you?" It was as if the thought had been carried with him through the sleep.

"No. Do you care about it so much?"

"I guess not." He stretched, and came across to her chair, dropping down beside her. "Listen, honey, I don't like to be curtailed like this, just because you see an element of risk. If I knew I couldn't go skating it would soon be that skating was the biggest factor in my life. I don't want you saying no all the time, either. I guess you'll have to ease up some of the time. Understand?"

"Yes." She realized her folly and timidity. For him there was no fear. He had only his own way of looking at the matter. "I won't ask you not to go again, Jeremy, but just be careful. Are you going today?"

"No. I gave up—long before that dinner knocked me out. It was to please you and for no other reason." He rubbed his face against hers.

"That was nice of you."

"But you see what I'm trying to say? What are you going to do when we get a family and they all want to go skating, swimming, riding, as they surely will? You can't go with them all the way, and can't stop them once they are away from your knee. You'll have to let go, darling." His voice was gentle but quite firm.

"I know, but that time is not yet. I'm just foolish, I suppose. I didn't mean to hurt you, Jeremy."

"You didn't . . . and we've both plenty to learn, so don't look so worried." He kissed her lips. "I love you more than anyone in the world, so don't get any of the wrong ideas, will you?"

"I won't," she promised soberly. He had warned her and she must heed the warning. He was not a man who could be tied to her apron strings. So far he had given way to her by his own will, but she must not press him too far. "I just don't want to be a widow again . . ." She was appalled as the careless words left her lips.

She flushed scarlet and bit her lips until they ached.

"That was scarcely warranted," he told her stiffly, getting to his feet.

"I don't know why I said it either. Forgive me. What's the matter with me today? I'm completely jittery and unlike myself." She felt confused, and afraid of where the confusion might lead them.

Jeremy turned away coldly. "You were thinking about Morgan then. You often do. Why?"

"In an abstract sort of way . . ." she spoke unhappily.

"Why? Why do you bring him into our life?"

"I don't know. I suppose I shall always blame myself . . . oh don't let's go into all that again. I think that dinner was too much for me too—I'll lie down for an hour. I don't know what's the matter with me today . . ." She left him abruptly, wondering why they were always on the verge of some revelation. Her nervous pacing continued until the room grew dark, for she could not rest. She heard Kate come into the kitchen, and Dan soon followed to help with the evening meal.

How could she meet them as if nothing had happened? Yet, what had happened? She washed her burning cheeks, laving them with the ice-cold water, but it did not cool the fever raging within her. She combed her hair, and powdered her face lavishly, glad to see that she looked much as usual. When Kate knocked on her door, calling out cheerfully that supper was ready, she went out and joined them.

Jeremy had evidently not stirred from his place by the stove, and after one sharp look he moved to the table. She knew that he was pleased she kept her poise in front of the others. She helped with the small talk during the meal, and later helped Kate with the chores.

"I'm going for a walk," Sylvia called, going for her heavy coat.

Jeremy was waiting for her at the outer door. "I'm coming with you."

"You needn't have bothered. I'm just wanting some air."

"You'd better wear something on your head. Take this scarf." He picked one off the rail. "What's the sense in getting cold?"

She walked swiftly into the night which

was darker than she had suspected. She slipped on a loose trunk of a tree. "Why can't Dan clear up as he goes? I might have broken a leg then," she complained.

Jeremy drew her arm beneath his and they walked more slowly into the night, until they gained the short lane that led directly down to the beach. The stones glistened frostily, every leaf and blade of grass had gained prominence as it became rimmed with silver thread.

They could not continue like this with so much unsaid between them. Sylvia glanced into his face, seeing the hard lines, the firm mouth. Jeremy looked impatient and she realized that he was still an unknown quantity. They might have walked for miles along the beach, had he not broken the silence.

"I suppose we're quarrelling politely?"

"It's my fault, Jeremy. I'm so miserable at times that I don't know what I'm saying. Lately—it's been worse, and I can't think why."

"Why are you miserable? Heaven knows I've tried to give you everything in my power. We're happy together, aren't we?

It's not that, is it?" She shook her head, unable to answer. "What's the matter?"

She felt his temper, scarcely restrained behind the hard words. "It's just—I can never be completely free . . ."

"Then for God's sake let's get to the bottom of everything and be done . . ."

"I always have to mind what I say—because you're so jealous of . . . Morgan, I suppose. Why are you?"

"Surely that's understandable? Is that the reason for this tension?"

"Some of it perhaps. I always feel that you are holding something back . . ."

"Well, where's the sense in telling you something that's sure to hurt? I just made up my mind to keep things to myself, that's all. You've enough to trouble you by the sound of things." He bit off the words savagely. "If you want to hear—then here it is. Don't forget I've tried to save you."

"It might help . . ." she whispered. Would she understand Jeremy better if she knew the secret that she had sensed? She waited, walking slowly beside him.

"Listen—you know most of it. We were young officers together in the Army . . . both prisoners of war . . . both got

186

wounded about the same time. Morgan got the head wound, mine was in my hip. That's not new? Well, after we got demobbed we didn't meet again for a couple of years . . . then one night in London . . ." he paused and she saw the effort it was to him to keep his voice even. "We met and teamed up for a spree. We'd both got too much money to spend—both meant to keep blind dates with a couple of girls. It was all right at first—but we both fancied the same girl. Ironical, wasn't it?" He paused, and looking down at her deliberately. "Want me to finish?"

She was white to the lips, so distressed that he hesitated. "Briefly—please."

"Well—there was a scrap . . . nothing more than we'd had a score of times. Morgan fell—hit his head where he'd been wounded. We were both found, blind drunk, the girls lifted our wallets and cleared out—and eventually Morgan recovered in hospital—but always had to wear the plate in his head. Now . . ."

"Then you were really responsible for—that?"

"I don't know." He shook his head. "I never will know. I know we scrapped but we were both beyond any real hard hitting by that time. Morgan was never an easy man to get on with. He fell . . . it was sheer bad luck he hit the one vital place . . ." he swallowed, unable to proceed.

"Oh, Jeremy . . ." She gripped his arm with both hands. "We both seem to be taking our happiness at Morgan's expense. What was between us all? When he died his mother said she would hold me morally responsible for his death—and I can't forget . . ." The words seemed to freeze on her cold lips.

"Blast her!" He shouted the words.

"But I'm really responsible, although it was an accident, wasn't it?"

"Wasn't mine an accident?" he looked at her uncertainly. "We're both building it into something."

"Were you blamed—at the time?" she asked.

"No. There wasn't anything anyone could do. Morgan was good-natured about the whole thing. We were both ashamed of ourselves afterwards."

"Just the—moral feeling that you— harmed him . . . ?"

"I suppose so. One carries a guilty conscience. Yours was an accident, wasn't it?"

She looked up, startled. "Of course it was—what do you mean?"

"I thought for a minute you were inferring something deeper. Why are we worrying so blasted much? I'm sorry about my share in his illness but what can I do? I'm not even sure that I *was* responsible."

"I wish you'd told me before."

"So that you could have had something more to worry you?" He spoke impatiently. "I wish I hadn't now. No sense in adding to what you've got—but you asked for it."

"Yes, I asked, didn't I?" She had asked on the last night of their honeymoon but he had not told her then. So much might have been saved them if he had been frank, for the knowledge that there was a secret between them had undermined their feeling for each other. "I begged his mother to retract her words to me, but she would not and I sometimes feel like a murderer. I can never get the scene with her out of my mind."

"Hell," he agreed. "Why're we in this together?"

"You—you said you both fancied the same girl . . . you still did, even after he married me."

The trembling words quivered in the still air.

Jeremy turned to her incredulously. "So that's what you're thinking . . . did I ever show my feeling for you, while Morgan was alive?"

"No."

"Then why put it like that?"

"Oh, I don't know." She pushed the scarf back from her dark hair, unable to think logically. "How awful it all is."

"Why don't you make allowances for yourself—and for me? None of it was intended. A sheer accident. Things like this do happen." He spoke jerkily, deeply disturbed.

"I wanted to tell you before—about the way his mother looked at it—but I couldn't. I can't get away from it, yet I can't live with it. You said the past was closed, but you've just proved that can never be. We're too close to each other and to the past to see things as they really are. It isn't finished as I'd hoped. You shouldn't have married me, Jeremy."

"Think so? I don't agree."

"Did you—did you marry me because you felt partly responsible . . ." she could not add to the words, but her meaning was terribly clear.

He lost his robust colour. "I married you for one reason only—because I loved you. I was mad about you from the first meeting, but I've nothing with which to reproach myself regarding that. Morgan never knew, and I'm certain you didn't guess either. Can you blame me for stepping in when he died? Can you?" He stopped and held her so that she had to meet his hard, blank gaze.

"I don't know. I wish the whole situation had not happened."

"Since it has—why can't you be reasonable and accept the inevitable? I wish to glory I hadn't told you now—but you've been so distressed as if you knew there was something . . ."

"That's it—as long as we have secrets of this kind we can't find complete happiness, Jeremy. I wish you'd told me sooner . . ."

"Or not at all." He spoke thinly, scowling down at her. "Listen, we're married and nothing that's been said changes that as far as I can see. We've got to find happiness within what we've got. You're emotional and worried because of something a bad-tempered old woman threw at you in a crazy moment. She was disappointed—granted, and troubled by his death . . . and she had to blame someone. It's not true, so why keep on about it, Sylvia? Be sensible. The two parts don't touch anywhere else—I've worked that out long ago. It's years since my part of it happened—I'd no idea you were ever likely to appear on the scene. It's just damn bad luck that it's worked out this way." He spoke persuasively, trying to change her attitude.

"I just can't forget that if Morgan had had a real chance he might have found happiness—I might still have been his wife. I can't follow the thought properly, but it tortures me. What evil thing was there between the three of us that it should have happened?"

"You told me you didn't love Morgan . . ." he reminded her, bitterly.

"I didn't—I was meaning to leave him . . ." she whispered brokenly. "Is that why it feels worse? He must have sensed my attitude; he would be terribly hurt. Oh, I wish I could get away somewhere by myself to think out all the implications. How can you expect me to be happy with so much between us? How can you, Jeremy? You come first and I care terribly—but it has to be right, or I can't bear to live with you. I want to understand myself as well as you. Oh, help me. I regret so much . . . how can one find peace?"

Jeremy's face was white and chilled. She felt his uncertainty and pain. "Sometimes one can't find peace. You will have to go on. We all have to go on when there is no returning. We can't put back the years. It's finished—we must live with what *is*. Nothing now can bring Morgan back."

"I can't go on," she whispered in despair, wondering why she felt so deadly tired. "Not any longer. It's getting too big for me. I've felt quite ill lately. I know I'm spoiling our life together, yet I can't change. It's like a curse . . ."

"What do you want me to do?"

"I don't know. I suppose I must lay my own ghosts for it's as if I were haunted."

"You've too much time in which to think," he told her harshly.

She laughed miserably. "What sort of life is it going to be if I never dare stop to think? I wish I could be by myself for a while."

"Listen, Sylvia, we're not parting . . ."

"Perhaps I needn't go away . . ." she hesitated. "But I want to be alone . . ."

"Are you wanting to finish with me?" His voice held a quality that puzzled her. "You're practically telling me that you can't make up your mind between the two of us."

"There you go again. Why are you so jealous of Morgan?" she spoke warily. "No it isn't that. I just ask for time to see my way clearly. Oh, don't take it the wrong way. It's you I love—it always has been. I didn't love Morgan."

"Yet you suggested, and not for the first time, that but for that unfortunate accident, Morgan might have been a different man—in which case presumably you would have been happy with him." The words came impetuously.

"Yes." Her anger rose red-hot to meet his. "If several things hadn't happened Morgan would have had his chance. I just don't know the answers and that is what I want to think about. But you won't grant me time . . ."

"Now we've got it clear—at last . . ."

"Don't shout."

"You forget you've got obligations to me . . ." he told her savagely.

"You're taking it too far, Jeremy. I do remember that love comes before all . . . there are no obligations between us, because we love each other."

They stared at each other, antagonism leaping between them. Sylvia put her hand to her head dazedly. Her face had gone pale, and she swayed.

"So you're walking out on me—too?" he sneered.

She looked at him incredulously. "Oh —what a terrible thing to say to me . . ."

"You're not talking to another woman now, you know," he said grimly.

"I—I feel absolutely ill with worry. I— can't think any more."

He took her arm. "Come along. We'll go back to the cabin. Oh, blast . . ."

They did not speak as they retraced their steps. Once inside Jeremy threw a log of wood into the stove, which had died down since Dan left the kitchen. A blaze of sparks spluttered out on to the floor, and he trod on them mechanically. Sylvia stood about, wondering what to do. She felt that she had burned her boats behind her in every sense of the expression, and knew she would have to pay for her impetuosity in bitter regret. Jeremy was a hard man in so many ways. While he loved her he could be swayed, but if he turned against her, life would be unbearable. Yet she had a right to ask for time to think, to plan their joint future. Until now he had not granted her time. If only she did not feel so confused and ill, she thought, with absolute exhaustion showing in her manner.

When he spoke he had his back to her. "That should keep the heat up for another hour or so. The atmosphere is low tonight. I'm sorry for that remark just now. Go to bed, Sylvia. I'll sleep in the small room tonight. Perhaps we can sort things out in the morning. We're both too upset to do it now. I don't want to quarrel with you

—that's the last thing in my mind. For God's sake try to get rid of your ghosts. This can't go on." His voice was hard, but she heard him thankfully.

"You don't mind, do you?" she whispered anxiously. He turned and deliberately met her gaze. "What do you think?"

5

AT the end of March the first guest arrived at the ranch. Sylvia welcomed her warmly, for she was glad of anything to take her mind off her own affairs. February had passed with leaden slowness, yet in some ways the time had flashed by. Preparing for Christine was a pleasant occupation, giving a meaning to their existence that had been lacking for many weeks.

"A funny time of the year to choose to come," Kate said sourly. "The leaves are not out yet, nor many of the flowers. What is there here to interest her?"

Christine had written to say that she was bringing her sketching materials as she wanted a working holiday, away from the coast. She hoped there would be some snow left as she wanted to capture the winter scene.

Sylvia realized that any true artist would appreciate the Kootenays at any time of the year. They were at their most delicate best in the light spring green raiment where the trees began to take shape and outline against the mountains. There was something in the shimmering light, in the floating shadows, the cold stirring of the lake, that brought a promise of warmer months. March was the month of fulfilment for the snow had largely gone, and the rivers were in flood. The land was filled with sound and energy and surging movement. Parts of the lake had been frozen over until the previous week, but that had gone now. Every time Jeremy went skating it was a small death to Sylvia, but she did not interfere. If she missed him for any considerable length of time she would look in the barn where he kept his skates, for he did not often trouble to tell her where or when he was going.

Matters had not grown better between them, for they had found no common ground on which they could meet. Jeremy continued to sleep in the spare room, and it seemed possible he would be there for ever. His mood against her was hard and unforgiving and she could find no way of breaking it down. They might have assumed a surface happiness but neither wished for that. They both knew that the matter must be dispensed with completely, and so far they had not been able to do this.

Sylvia was so actively unhappy that she felt like leaving the ranch, but so far had not been able to summon up courage to do so. Jeremy would never forgive such an action, she knew. While they stayed together there was hope for the future. Apart they would drift further into the misunderstanding. It was into this atmosphere that Christine was coming. Sylvia's heart sank at the thought.

She helped Kate to prepare the cabins in readiness for the Easter invasion. She hoped for a busy time to help to keep thought at bay. Only in work could either she or Jeremy find alleviation for their estrangement. Jeremy was working hard out of doors, although the ground was still iron hard. He took some punishment that spring, and Dan condemned him, and spat angrily on the ground, bewildered by what was happening.

Sylvia knew that Jeremy was as miserable as she was, and the knowledge that she had added to his burden, hurt her afresh. The cabins were all ready, as bright as on the day they were first built, when Christine arrived by car.

Sylvia was interested, in her, realizing that they were about of an age. Christine had short, curly hair cut cleverly in a windswept bob which suited her dainty features. She was tall, thin, almost angular, but with a way of walking that was beautiful. Her husky voice was warm, and her passion for painting was almost an obsession. She wore bright colours, gay beads, often appearing in trousers. Her character was gay and open, engagingly frank. Sylvia was won over at once as she showed her to the cabin prepared for her.

"I do hope you'll be comfortable here—and happy with us."

"I'm always happy," Christine observed, glancing around her. "I like this because it's so light. North light, too . . . yes, it'll do very well. I mean to be out of doors as much as I can, but occasionally I'll work in here. You won't mind that, will you?"

"Of course not. You are quite a well-known person, aren't you? We have seen your name in magazines several times this winter," Sylvia remarked.

Christine laughed easily. "Yes—all helps. I'm nearly dead on my feet from over-work, as a matter of fact. I've been in Hollywood, doing scenes for a film. Fascinating but killing. I want to get a few pictures of this district and send them on in a week or two. But first—a rest . . ." She yawned and put both arms over her head in a lovely gesture.

"I'll prepare a meal," Sylvia promised. "You know where everything is?"

"Oh, yes, thanks. I'll just unpack and then come along." She turned aside to her baggage, which Dan had brought in to the cabin. "How's Jeremy? I haven't seen him yet."

"He's around somewhere," Sylvia replied, a little surprised at the use of Jeremy's first name. "I expect he'll be in for the meal and you'll see him then. Don't be long."

Christine changed swiftly into a purple velvet suit that looked handsome with her golden hair, and she entered the main cabin half an hour later with Jeremy, having caught up with him as he returned from the fruit garden.

"I'm looking forward to a wonderful rest," Christine spoke zestfully. "Would you take me out on the lake one day, Jeremy? I want to get a scene of this side of the shore, and think it would be a splendid idea to do it from a boat."

"You could get the same effect from the jetty, couldn't you?" Kate suggested.

"Not enough distance," Christine dismissed the words airily. "I want to get a large scene . . . I've something in mind."

Sylvia served the meal, eating scarcely anything herself for she felt almost ill with apprehension. Already the atmosphere was changing, for Christine dominated the whole table. Jeremy was amused with her enthusiasm, and promised to cooperate in any way he could.

"But I'm a busy man these days," he warned. "Lots to do on the ranch."

Christine smiled at him, before turning to Sylvia. "You two are awfully happy, aren't you? When I was here before you were in hospital, Sylvia. Better now?"

"Yes, thank you." Sylvia turned the conversation determinedly, with Kate aiding and abetting. Kate did not like Christine and her manner was off-hand.

When the meal was over Sylvia tackled Kate. "I do hope you'll be kind to Christine, Kate . . . please. We want her to stay as long as she can. If she likes it here she may even bring other guests. Don't forget that it's all part of our planning for the future."

Kate looked at her sulkily. "All right. I'll remember. But why you want her here beats me. She shouldn't be on the loose without a fellow of her own."

"That's enough, Kate." Sylvia was so displeased that she moved away quickly. "Don't go too far."

Kate banged the pans around trying to work off her ill-humour. "Some folks can only see as far as the end of their own noses, and that's a fact."

"Christine's nose is a very pretty one," Sylvia deliberately misunderstood the redoubtable Kate, and went out laughing. "Yes, Jeremy—what is it?"

"Don't you think there should be some heat in Christine's cabin?" Jeremy came towards her as she hurried across to their own cabin. "It's pretty cold."

"Yes, I agree. Take one of the oil stoves over."

Jeremy went to the barn where they were stored, and presently she saw him taking the stove over to Christine's brightly lighted cabin. He stayed to light the stove and left it burning. Sylvia could hear their voices raised in friendly give and take.

"The nights are cold. My wife thinks you should have this in case of need."

"Lovely. Thank you, Jeremy. I'm a warm person as a rule. Still, I may be glad of it. Show me how to light it again, in case it goes out."

She bent down near him, and her short curls touched his face. Jeremy drew back quickly, but showed her the mechanism of the stove. She promised to turn it up if she needed more warmth.

"I mean to work, but I want to have some fun, too," Christine told him restlessly. "I want a change. Let's have dancing one night. It's so quiet . . ."

"You knew what it was like when you came," Jeremy retreated to the door, laughing. "How'd you like to dance with Dan?"

"Sooner dance with you," she told him, watching him. "Don't you dance?"

"I used to. We seem to get out of that sort of thing with living in the country. I've an idea you are going to find this too quiet for you."

Her gaze sought his. "Maybe not. You never can tell."

Jeremy went out, smiling grimly, and Sylvia drew a breath of relief. Christine was fascinating, and to a man must be very appealing. Her light was soon out and they realized that she was probably as genuinely tired as she had said she was.

Christine usually wore trousers during the daytime, as less impeding to progress when she wanted to scramble about the rocks in search of copy. In the evenings she would change into more feminine wear, when she was a delight to the eye.

Jeremy was pressed into willing service, to show her the best places for her work, and he would often drive her in her car to some distant vantage point. When Sylvia saw the results of these expeditions she was forced to admit that Christine had a genuine talent. She was able to capture a mood, a grey rock, a stormy sky, the distant gathering storm, in a way that was uncanny. Her cabin grew stacked with canvases, many unfinished.

"I'll do them one day," Christine promised airily. "I often work fast like this and then finish them off at home. It's more fun that way."

"She's another of the rich playgirls," Kate said acidly. "Too much money in my opinion."

"Yet she works hard," Sylvia defended her idly.

"Because it suits her at the moment. Awful the way money gets distributed. She's got plenty. That dress tonight was too fancy for here."

"Oh, Kate, nothing is too grand if you are happy wearing it. I thought it was an absolutely beautiful dress."

"Why don't *you* get some new clothes?" Kate stood with arms akimbo, staring at Sylvia as if she were seeing her for the first time.

"Don't you like my clothes?"

"Nice enough—but get a dress like the one she wore tonight," urged Kate. "We're not the only ones who thought it mighty pretty."

The words troubled Sylvia, and she glanced hard into the woman's eyes. Without answering she left the cabin and returned to her own. She sank into the first chair she came to, trembling. How could Jeremy help admiring someone as lovely as Christine? It was the most natural thing in the world. Had he been a happy man she could have teased him about it; as it stood the situation held all the elements of tragedy. The thought struck through to her heart, making it ache. Her own looks were eclipsed as if some of the inner worry were taking a toll of her strength. She glanced into the mirror and the fear in her eyes made her look again.

"Why am I afraid? I don't think I'm really afraid in spite of what Kate says. No, it's deeper than that. Jeremy would never forget . . . what is my duty? I can't just—rescue Jeremy. He would resent that."

Neither could she ask Christine to leave. She was much too nice a person to understand hints. The situation must be allowed to develop along its own lines. Daily, Christine and Jeremy set out together, searching the countryside for the scenes that Christine considered necessary before she could relax. One evening they had an impromptu dance, rolling up the carpets, and dancing to records. It was fun, and Sylvia enjoyed it as much as anyone. They had grown so quiet and sober that she realized they had needed stirring up.

"Not often a man has two such pretty partners," Jeremy said.

Sylvia's colour was high, and her brilliant brown eyes were shining. She had enjoyed dancing with Jeremy. Christine hurried to place another record on the stand.

"More—more . . ." she cried as each dance ended. "I can dance all night."

"More than we can," Jeremy told her finally. "We get up at six, my lady."

She pouted. "It's only midnight."

Jeremy laughed at her disappointment, and yawned pointedly. "Just the same—off you go."

Sylvia wondered how Christine would take such a summary dismissal, but she did not appear to mind. She went out laughing to herself, and presently they saw her light go on, and knew she was safely in her cabin.

"That was fun, Jeremy," Sylvia drew near to him. "I enjoyed it. Perhaps we ought to have a holiday together some time . . ."

"Not much future in that right now," he told her, watching her. "Is there?"

She turned aside, hurt by his tone. "Perhaps not. I wouldn't know."

His attitude was so cold that she was unable to see behind the façade he had built between them. He watched her as she went over to her own room. While Christine had been with them no one would have guessed his feeling, but now he let Sylvia know his utter implacability.

She sighed and closed the door, not strong enough to battle with him. Yet he was spoiling for a fight, she thought uneasily. He would have enjoyed a quarrel. Was he right? Would a quarrel clear the air for them both? She was unequal to such a thing, and dreaded that he might start a row that would finally part them.

I wish I was anywhere but here for a while, she thought rebelliously. She could not see her way clear, or plan the future. They had reached a deadlock.

Now that Kate's suspicions had been planted in her own mind, Sylvia found herself watching Jeremy's growing interest in the young artist. She could not find anything wrong, and persuaded herself that Kate was mistaken. Jeremy went about his work much as usual, his quietness no deeper than it had been since their quarrel and parting.

Christine was the frankest person imaginable, and would spend hours with anyone who had the time to spare for her. When she was working she did not appear to need any company but her own. She painted Dan as he stood with a spade in his hand, looking like part of the good earth he loved. It was an excellent likeness and captured the old man's dry humour. Christine promised it would be exhibited.

Dan was delighted, and Kate declared that he was assuming airs above his station. Christine enjoyed the attention she received for she was their only guest, and they all concentrated on her in their various ways.

"I love it here," she cried one morning after breakfast, as she stood waiting for

Sylvia to dress so that they could go out together.

"Glad you do." Kate was washing dishes with a clatter. "When do you plan to go back to Vancouver?"

"Not for at least another month. I'm free and there is plenty of scope for me here. I shall keep bobbing up from time to time, so you won't finish with me when I leave." She smiled sweetly for she was well aware why Kate had asked the question. Sylvia joined them, clad in a long coat, and looking rather washed out, Kate thought. "Ready? I'd like to go swimming today, but Jeremy tells me it is too chilly yet for the likes o' me. Do you agree?"

They fell into step on the path. "It's too cold unless you are used to going in the water all the year round. Jeremy is right. A lake this size never warms up, Christine. I wouldn't advise it either, but don't listen to me if you want to try it out. Just don't get drowned, that's all."

"Oh, Jeremy promised to keep an eye on me—but perhaps it is too cold."

Sylvia did not answer. Jeremy's easy-going friendship was based on a firm foundation and she was determined not to worry. He was in a strange mood but would pull out of it in time, she hoped.

They heard a shattering sound that made them both jump. Dan dropped some boxes he was carrying into the packing shed. They had cleared the shed the previous day but had been rained off before everything could be put back.

"That man!" Christine hissed. "He'd drop his own head if it were loose." She smiled at him enchantingly. "Good morning, Dan. What sort of a day is it?"

"Fine. Just right after the rain. You won't need macs."

"We're going down for the mail. Want anything from the store?" It was her usual question, but as Dan never bought anything from week to week it was not surprising that he refused. Christine and Sylvia set out at a sharp pace, for the air was cool.

"This is the most straightforward place I ever struck." Christine walked with her hands in her pockets to keep warm. "Two roads only—so you know where you're going. This one to the store, that one to Grey Creek. I wish life were so well defined."

"Don't you think it might grow monotonous?" Sylvia liked the girl and knew that under happier circumstances they would have been friends. As it was they were more to each other than mere hostess and guest.

"No. I like straightforward things best. I like people to know what they want and go after it. It's the subtleties that get me down." Christine spoke energetically. "Sylvia, you don't really mind if I swim with Jeremy, do you?"

"Of course not. What an odd question, Christine. I think it would be much wiser than going alone. Have you arranged anything?" Sylvia tried to speak naturally and as frankly as Christine had done. She was determined not to read more into the situation than was there.

"Not exactly, but he said last night he'd take me. Why not come along?"

Sylvia shook her head and shivered. "Much too cold for me yet."

"Jeremy goes regularly, doesn't he?" Christine looked at Sylvia questioningly.

"Yes—in all but the worst weather." Sylvia was glad to pass on to something else and she began to ask questions about life on the coast where Christine lived. By the time they reached the store her former serenity of mind had returned to her. The man who was acting postmaster had their mail sorted and ready, and he passed it to Sylvia with a smile.

"You folks get plenty mail these days."

"I'm a very popular person," Christine put in. "I've lots of friends, bless 'em."

Sylvia treasured her words, feeling that if Christine had so many friends, she would not be likely to take Jeremy seriously.

During the afternoon she knew that they went swimming together. The lake was like a long streak of grey iron, absolutely chill and stark, and Sylvia wondered how Christine could enjoy the chilly scene. Jeremy made no mention of the fact on his return, beyond handing her his towel to dry near the stove. Christine did not come in with him. He assumed I knew all about it, Sylvia thought afterwards, and would not comment in case it impressed the incident on his mind. He liked Christine but she was certain that was as far as it went with him. They appeared to be drifting further apart with each day that dawned, and the knowledge saddened her unbearably. She felt she needed his understanding more now than ever before, and she wondered what she ought to do. Pride held her back, just as it was holding him, she thought, and there was nowhere that they seemed able to converse, or hold even the briefest of talks.

She learned most of the business of the ranch through the conversations that Dan and Jeremy had at breakfast, or she would have known little to help her through that spring. She realized that Jeremy was as unhappy as she was, and she longed for them to be able to patch up their relationship. Jeremy had made it clear that patching would not do. It must be the whole new garment—or none at all. So she hesitated, unsure of everything in the situation.

Sylvia felt that she was measuring the slow passage of time by her own feeling. The days were lengthening, the air still cold, but the sun was rising higher each day, bringing warmth and colour to the Kootenays.

Often Christine and Jeremy went off for

long walks, Jeremy carried the box with Christine's paints and easel. She always brought the results to Sylvia or Kate for their approval or criticism, disarming them by this simple manoeuvre.

She's after his scalp, Kate told herself disagreeably. She can't kid me.

I wish something would give, Sylvia thought wearily one day as she helped Kate to prepare supper. The tension was mounting between them all, and she felt that she was no longer thinking properly. If Jeremy were honourable he would realize where his conduct would lead him, and possibly others. She blamed him strongly for he was older, and a married man, and she must soon pull him up if he did not change. It was difficult, for they seldom met these days.

The matter came to a head the following morning in a way she had not been prepared for. Christine and Jeremy had arranged to go to Creston together to do some necessary shopping. Jeremy waited impatiently at the gate, while Christine got ready, and he sounded the horn impatiently when she delayed to join him. Sylvia realized that at any time his patience was limited but it was exceedingly short this morning.

He got out of the car and strode to the cabin, knocking imperatively on the door. Sylvia did not know why she waited to see what would happen next for she loathed spying in any form, but she did wait, arrested by some inner warning, as Christine came to the door and threw it open laughingly.

She was dressed in a green corduroy suit with a saucy green pointed hat on her hair, a bright red feather standing straight up, looking rather like a female Robin Hood. She was strikingly lovely even at a distance and no one could blame Jeremy for admiring her beauty.

Jeremy, well aware that he was being watched, and in a reckless mood, murmured: "Stunning. You're mighty pretty this morning, Christine." He was smiling broadly.

Christine stood in front of him, revelling in his open admiration. She pirouetted gaily round him so that he could view her new suit. Jeremy grinned, a mischievous light in his eyes. He was obviously amused, Sylvia thought.

"Do you like me, Jeremy?"

"You're much too pretty for an old married man like me," he said lightly.

Christine approached closer, and without warning threw both arms round his neck. Jeremy had not been prepared for such a response, and dull colour rose in his face. He drew back stiffly, his hands grasping her wrists, and bringing them down from his shoulders.

"That's enough," he growled, angry that Sylvia had seen this. He dropped Christine's wrists and turned away. "Why on earth did you do that?"

"You're so handsome and I felt like kissing someone. Dan is so uninteresting, isn't he?" She spoke plaintively, disarming him at once.

"All right. Don't try it on again, that's all." He had no thought for her just then as he strode ahead to the car, for he realized that Sylvia might have misconstrued what was, in his opinion, a girlish and impulsive action.

Even from a distance Sylvia had realized that Jeremy was embarrassed by Christine's kiss, and she noticed the finality in his attitude. She did not stay to see any more but went indoors, pondering what to do. It was time to call a halt.

Christine might not yet be in love with Jeremy, but she was on the verge of it. Sylvia could not bear to examine her own feelings, or to wonder if Jeremy might be turning to Christine through sheer recklessness. They were each being driven on by forces outside their control.

"If I could only be sure . . ." she sighed.

She waited supper for him that evening. Usually she would not have paid him that courtesy, preferring to have hers with the others when he was late, but tonight she meant to talk to him alone. Usually he went outside as soon as he had finished his meal and there was never any chance of private conversation. She knew that he was working in a part of the garden that had never been dug over before. Something in the hard spadework appealed to him in his present state of mind. It was some distance from the cabin and possibly he could not hear the gong, or having heard it he might not wish to join them.

She sat with her elbows on the table, waiting patiently. Jeremy was rapidly reaching a frame of mind where he would do something harmful, and she must choose her words carefully. She thought back carefully across his career as he had sketched it for her, and knew that she was dealing with a man impatient of all restriction. The only way to persuade Jeremy was through his love for her—yet his actions pointed to the fact that he no longer cared what happened to her. The thought frightened her. She had not intended the misunderstanding to go as far as it had. She had reckoned without that steel in Jeremy's nature. She must be the first to give in.

She wondered if his interest in Christine were genuine, or assumed for reasons of his own. It could so quickly become real between a man and a woman. The girl was spirited and pretty, and was willing to meet him more than half way. Sylvia wondered if she had now the right to interfere when her own life with Jeremy had been such a complete failure. The thought was paramount as she watched him striding across the clearing towards the dining cabin.

He entered and saw her, and she felt that he was not pleased.

She tried to make her greeting casual. "Hullo, Jeremy. I haven't eaten either. I waited for you. There is some fresh coffee." She was glad that Kate had left.

He went to the sink and turned on the tap. "I'm covered in earth."

"You are busy these days." Now they were talking she didn't want to stop, to drop back into one of the silences that came so easily. "Isn't it still rather cold to be turning over that patch just now?"

He shrugged indifferently. "Does it matter?"

"I think so. It would be better to wait for the milder weather."

"We shall need it for a fresh strawberry crop next season." He made the explanation without interest, but the thought warmed her for she realized that he was looking ahead. He came to the table and sat down. She handed him a cup of coffee and pushed the newly baked rolls nearer to him. "Thank you."

They began the meal, and she was determined not to speak of anything of a controversial nature until he had finished.

Jeremy had a way of losing interest in food when a discussion threatened. She sensed his curiosity and knew that he was expecting her to mention what had happened that morning at Christine's cabin.

After the salad she cut him a generous portion of fruit pie, glad to see that he ate it as if he enjoyed it. When he had finished he reached for a cigarette and passed the case to her. He merely nodded when she shook her head, and lighted his own.

"Do you mind if we talk? We can be private here for a while." Her distressed manner made him glance up.

"I'm not very interested, Sylvia. What I do is my own affair. You decided your line of action some time ago and you'd better stick to that. I simply don't understand how two persons feeling as we—did, can have come to feel as we feel now. Let's leave it at that."

"This is my affair, too, Jeremy . . . when it goes as far as seeing Christine kissing you."

"It was the first time." His voice was sarcastic. "What do you think I am?"

She knew she was antagonizing him by

the wrong approach. There could be no half measures with Jeremy. He demanded her full trust or nothing. "Was it fair to me?"

"Why not? You don't care one way or the other." He smoked rapidly, flicking the ash from the cigarette with quick, nervous gestures.

"Don't I? We are very awry, aren't we? Isn't there anything we can do to straighten things out again? And do you think it is quite fair to play with Christine's emotions in this manner? She's a perfectly nice person."

"How do you know I'm playing with her emotions?" He spoke grimly.

"Because I cannot believe that you are serious. As a married man you must know the danger for her."

"She doesn't seem to mind."

"But you're older—and married," she reminded him.

"Exactly what does that amount to? Really, let's stop beating about the bush."

She coloured warmly but stood her ground. "I expect you to behave properly to our guests . . ."

"Who says I am not?" His voice held a warning ring that made her shiver.

"You leave me no other course than to ask Christine to leave." She choked over the words, determined not to look at him, for his anger was leaping up.

"If you do that I'll leave with her. You're making this into something. What's the matter with you? You've no right to interfere."

"You—gave me the right when you married me."

"You handed it right back the day we quarrelled."

"Oh, Jeremy!" She realized the bitterness behind his words. She had hurt him unbearably. "I don't know what to do, or say. I'm not sure of anything except that this association with Christine must stop. Has it gone very far?"

"If you mean are we lovers—definitely not." He was shouting but she was thankful to hear the denial.

"I'm glad about that. I've been so jealous today that I don't want to live through such a storm of feeling again."

He looked at her quickly, surprised by the admission. "You—jealous?"

"Yes. Fantastic, isn't it?"

They were both quiet, seeming to have come to the end of what there was to say. Sylvia wished that she knew what he was thinking.

"What made you jealous? You must have seen that it was not I who invited the kiss this morning."

Sylvia knew that she must answer him truthfully even if he misunderstood. "You see Jeremy, in spite of the way things are with us, I do care terribly what happens to you."

"You're talking this way out of a sense of duty. You've no need to sacrifice yourself on any such altar. I get on very well alone. Please keep away from Christine. I don't want an outsider to be dragged into what is purely a private affair."

She watched him go to the door, and open it. In another moment he would be gone and it would be too late. Even now she could keep him at her side if she wished, could regain some of the devotion that had once been showered on her. She dismissed the thought, for later he might resent it. Jeremy wanted her full trust or nothing. She spoke his name involuntarily.

226

"Jeremy . . ."

"Well?"

She took a step towards him. "I'm so miserable."

"Whose fault is that?" But he did not go. He closed the door and returned to her.

"Mostly my own fault, but a little is yours, too. You must see that. I can't bear to go on just to be unhappy like this all the time."

"How can you change what can't be altered? It was you who kept the past alive, not I."

"If we can't be right with each other I must go away where I can't see you."

"Nonsense. Where can you go?"

"I don't have to stay here. I don't wish to go on living like this. Will you never be able to forgive me?" Her words were so low and gentle that he scarcely heard them. "If only you would forgive me it would be something to build on. It's knowing that in your heart you despise me . . ."

"I don't," he protested.

"You despise my attitude—you're impatient with it, anyhow. I'm still in the wrong. Try to see it from my point of view. I'd no idea it would grow as big as this. I never meant you to feel pushed out; we've gone from bad to worse, yet I care for you. I can't take any more. Your attitude now is terrible. Won't you forgive me?" She was so agitated that she sat down, trembling violently.

Jeremy walked up and down the room. It was unlike him to show nervous strain and she realized that they were both overwrought. "Yes . . . I forgive you," he said finally. "There's nothing to forgive; we've made a hash of our marriage. I was so sure of you at first. I couldn't believe that we'd ever grow like other couples. I should have kept silent about my own part, then we might never have grown so awry. You full of remorse, I full of jealousy—queer combination, isn't it? But that's not all of it now. You chose to separate from me . . ."

"Yes, I was wrong there. It should never have been allowed to come to this. I take all the blame, Jeremy. I can hardly remember where it all started." She looked down sadly at the tablecloth, not able to see for tears.

"Your mistake was in turning me out," he told her bluntly.

"I'm sorry. Oh, if you knew how sorry. It isn't what you think, either . . ."

He watched her gravely. All the temper had died in him. There was depression in his bearing that hurt her unbearably. "If it's Christine that's worrying you she doesn't count—you know she never could." he said wearily. "We talk for ever and we don't get anywhere. We seem to make matters worse."

He strode to the door again, anxious to be done with the scene. She saw that although he professed to forgive her there was no genuine softening in his attitude. He might forgive her, for he cared enough to ease her mind on the point, but he had not forgotten. It would be many a long weary day before he would forget.

She was appalled as he strode straight over to the car, knowing he would probably drive to Grey Creek or Creston, and come home feeling more cheerful after a visit to some of his cronies.

His attitude left her no choice. He was limping badly and she knew that he must be tired, for it never showed otherwise.

What more could she do? He would not forgive interference between himself and Christine, for in spite of his assertion that Christine did not count, she knew he respected and liked the girl.

On leaden feet she returned to their cabin, and prepared for bed. Jeremy came in about half past eleven and threw himself down on the narrow bed in the small room. She had listened for that creaking movement every night for the past six or seven weeks. It sickened her, and she would be done with it.

She rose silently and began to collect her clothes. One candle was all the illumination she allowed herself as she filled both trunks, and left them to be strapped in the daylight. The suitcase she meant to take with her.

She looked into the living-room, collecting what she could see of hers. The room looked comfortable, the inanimate objects came alive as the candle flickered over them. Sylvia realized that it was not her own action that would be final, it was what followed. She was putting all of their joint future into Jeremy's hands, and he would know this. On his action now would rest their future lives and happiness. If he cared he could do something about that future; if he did not, it would let him out. Either way she had to be certain. Theirs was not a marriage that could be patched up as he had said; it must be riveted this time with steel that would not break.

It was almost three o'clock when she stole from the cabin and took the suitcase out to the car. She went softly and knocked on Kate's door.

"Good lord!" She heard Kate mutter in consternation. "Who is it this time o'night?"

"Kate, can you come for a moment?" Sylvia did not wish to be overheard.

Kate looked weird in a purple dressing-gown with a silken cord tied hastily around her middle to keep it together. "You're sick? Maybe something the matter with Dan?" She stood aside to allow Sylvia to enter.

"No." Sylvia was not sure how far she dared trust to Kate's discretion. She could not leave without trace, for they might all be seriously alarmed if they could not find her. "I'm—leaving for a while, Kate. Will you try to manage? You know what there is to do. Try to continue as if I were here."

Kate's raven hair streaked across her brow and she pushed it back impatiently. Sylvia was sorry to have wakened her from sleep in such a manner but her need had been imperative. "Funny time of night to be leaving. I'll make you a cup of tea."

"I haven't time for that, thank you. I'm going now. I'll take the car as far as Locker and leave it in front of Mrs. Dell's house. Jeremy can pick it up there when he wishes. He has a key too, so I'll lock it. Do you understand?"

"You're running off? I thought you would. You can't stand competition, can you?" Kate stared boldly across at her.

"It isn't quite that. Once I thought so, but what I'm trying to do now may solve our trouble—one way or the other."

"Where are you going? I'd better know."

Sylvia hesitated. Already the first beams of the new day were throwing the shadows back and she could see the cabin clearly through the open door. "Kate, if I tell you will you promise not to tell anyone unless it is imperative?"

"You want to give your husband a scare?" The words held contempt.

"No—but if he wants me back he must send for me. It's this way, Kate—I want to give him every chance *not* to send for me if that's the way he feels. It's nothing to do with Christine either. I'm just not sure about anything any more. I never will be now unless he makes the first move. Don't you see—this is his chance and mine, which ever way he moves. I must be sure—we must both be sure now. I have a special reason for needing to be sure."

"Something in that," Kate looked at her thoughtfully, noting her agitation. "You must know in your own mind that Christine couldn't hold him for long. It was something that happened long before she came, wasn't it?"

"Yes. Christine only complicates it further. I want to give Jeremy plenty of time to think straight. When I'm out of the way he'll be reasonable. Perhaps he'll want me back and perhaps he won't. I honestly do not know. My thinking is muddled. He must decide."

"So you're going—where?" Kate whistled expressively when Sylvia told her.

"You are certainly going far enough. How will he catch up with you there?"

"That's his affair—and you forget—he may not wish to catch up with me." Sylvia was anxious to get away, for Dan was an early riser and she had no wish to have to make the explanations a second time. "Don't forget—you are not to tell him unless it's absolutely essential."

"I won't—I promise." Moved by a sudden impulse Kate drew the girl to her. "I wish you all the good luck in the world; you could do with it."

Sylvia drove away rapidly, in the direction of Locker, meeting no one on the silent roads. It was strange being out at that hour, flitting through the shadows that still lingered, hearing the whisper of furry animals that raced ahead of her into the woods.

In front of Mrs. Dell's ranch she locked the car and slung her suitcase to the ground. She would wait here to meet the first bus in to Creston.

When Jeremy sauntered in to breakfast that morning, Kate was standing by the stove, frowning at nothing in particular.

234

As Christine was often late, Kate had taken her a tray, hoping by this means to keep the girl in her cabin for a while. She was glad that Dan had eaten his meal and gone about his chores as usual. She felt it was a stroke of luck that she was alone with Jeremy.

He sat down at the table. "Good morning, Kate."

"Good morning." She put a plate of porridge in front of him but he shook his head.

"I couldn't—not this morning. Any bacon?"

"Yes." She replaced the porridge with the bacon and a tomato, and a slice of fried bread. "That do?"

"Thank you. Where is everyone?"

"Dan had his ten minutes ago. He's gone to look at the water box, I think. It was overflowing last night and he thinks something is lodging in it." Kate stood with her hands on her big hips, watching him.

"I'll go along later. Has . . . Mrs. Lang had hers?" He was eating rapidly as he spoke.

"No." Kate spoke the negative with considerable innuendo.

"Oh? Why not?" Something in her expression arrested his attention.

Kate shrugged strong shoulders; it was not for her to tell him. She watched as he tried to finish his breakfast, but the food had gone dry in his mouth and he did not finish. He pushed the plate aside, and presently sauntered out into the sunshine. She watched interestedly through the window as he made his way straight over to the cabin he had just left. If he were half a man, she thought contemptuously, he'd have known that his wife was not in the bedroom.

Jeremy entered impetuously. "Sylvia!" he shouted. He entered her room without ceremony, seeing the neatly made bed, the trunks locked, but not corded. His face whitened and he looked round for some note of explanation. There was nothing although he ransacked the whole cabin. Every sign of her presence there had gone. He raced back across the clearing to the kitchen where Kate awaited him.

"You know something about this. Sylvia

has left the ranch." He stood close to Kate, his eyes cold and challenging.

"What else did you expect her to do?" Kate's tone was acid.

"That's enough. Where is she?"

"Would I know?" Kate moved out of range.

"I think you would. She might tell you. She's not the sort to just walk out without a word. Has she gone somewhere within the ranch? Tell me what you know."

Kate saw his agitation and felt sorry for him; sorry for the whole sordid business. It certainly was not in character for Sylvia to walk off without a word. She never tried to hurt anyone deliberately. "I can't tell you. She asked me not to unless it was essential . . . and I promised."

"My God, woman . . ." His anger boiled up white hot. "Get out of my way. She must be somewhere in the vicinity."

"She said she'd leave your car in front of Mrs. Dell's," Kate said thoughtfully.

"Then she's gone some distance?" He stared at her. "Kate, what you know you'd better tell me." His voice dropped a note, and she felt the menace there. He was not as easy-going as he sometimes appeared on the surface.

"I promised . . ." she spoke uneasily.

"If you don't tell me I'll have you in front of a Judge," he threatened.

"What will you do if I tell you?"

"Fetch her back, of course. What do you think?" Kate considered the words. It was what she thought he should do, but neither she nor Sylvia had been sure that he would. "She's gone to your stepmother and brother in England—flying. She thought she'd put enough distance between you both for a bit to allow you to cool down. That's the truth—I swear it," she added.

Jeremy left her, forgetting to thank her. He returned to their cabin, sitting down while he thought out his first move. He realized the meaning behind her flight instantly, for they had failed each other in their marriage.

He saw the trunks, awaiting transport, and his lips tightened. He had no intention of shipping those, whatever the outcome. He threw some of his clothes into a holdall that had come out to Canada with him, and put on a pan of water to heat for shaving. After that he counted what loose money he had in the cabin, and took it across to Kate.

"This should just about carry you through until we return. If need be sign for what you want at the store. I'll be back in a week or so, all being well."

"What happens about the guests?" Kate asked blankly.

He considered the question with only half his attention. He was coming back and might need money; the guests were part of the future they'd planned for. "No one due for a few weeks, is there? Can't you cope?"

"What'll I do about Christine?"

"Let her stay as long as she wishes. You know what she pays. Try to manage, Kate. We'll be back."

Kate's stern face softened. "Sure and I'll cope. Don't worry."

"I won't—now I know where she is. Say good-bye to Dan and Christine for me, will you? Explain as little as you possibly can."

"Leave it to me," Kate said briskly. "I should have been a diplomat."

Jeremy left the ranch twenty minutes later,

without seeing Christine. He strode down the lane, soon covering the ground in to Locker. The holdall was not heavy and he had plenty to think about as he strode along. He drove the car from Mrs. Dell's gate as far as Creston, where he drew a considerable sum of money. His passport was still in order, and had recently been renewed. He changed some money into travellers' cheques and after that luck was against him for he missed his train and had to wait half a day for the next one to take him as far as Calgary.

Meantime, Kate gloried in explaining as little as possible to a thoroughly mystified Christine. The girl appeared, still yawning and sleepy, explaining that she had sat up late, painting a scene before she forgot the brilliance of the colours. She was surprised to find that she was minus both host and hostess.

"I can't understand—Jeremy never breathed a word of it to me. Why did they go off without saying a word?"

"They told me to say good-bye," Kate planked a cup of hot coffee in front of her.

"Did they know last night? It's rather

—odd, isn't it? Must be something urgent that cropped up—or have they quarrelled?" She glanced up at Kate speculatively, measuring her strength and finesse. She could get anything she wanted out of Kate if she cared to try. She smiled into the cup as she sipped the coffee. "Poor Jeremy."

"Poor nothing," Kate snorted, offended. She had allowed Christine to suppose that they left the ranch together.

"Where are they?" Christine asked curiously.

"Gone to England. Maybe someone is ill. How would I know?"

"I think you would—and do," Christine said gently. "It isn't as if they mean to be back tomorrow, either. I can't understand Jeremy not telling me . . ." Christine's beautiful hair was swept back from her face, and she looked tired.

"And why should he tell you?" Kate's hackles rose visibly. She felt that daylight needed letting in somewhere. "It need not make any difference to you; you can stay on as long as you wish. I'll see to *you*."

Christine smiled again. "Thank you, but I won't stay. I'll leave now and come back later when they return. I've plenty of work for the moment."

"Sit down," Kate said slowly, gathering for the attack.

She might have known Christine hadn't relinquished her hold on Jeremy. She was meaning to return for another go later, and the whole business would start again. Kate didn't like it.

"No, I'll go and pack, I think. I could leave my heavy case. When did you say they would be back?" She looked discontented.

"I didn't say." Kate's voice hardened. "Sit down."

"I think you forget yourself, Kate."

"I'm forgetting nothing," Kate thundered. "Sit down . . . and listen to me."

Christine left the window and sat down, because she must. Kate was a formidable adversary even in good temper. "I shan't forget this . . ."

"No—neither will I. You won't forget what I'm going to say to you, either." Kate got into her stride without preamble. "You think you're going to run off because you might be bored without Jeremy to trip around with you. You've been concentrating on him, haven't you? You forgot he was another woman's husband. Your line's been complete frankness; you disarmed them both with that. It kept *her* quiet, because she's not your type. She can't stand up for what she knows is right, but I'm a-doing it right now. You never took me in—not for a minute. I've met your sort before. Sit down . . ."

"Really!" Christine was growing frightened, and wished Dan would come. The silence outside was oppressive.

Kate read her thoughts and shrugged. "You thought to go now—and sneak back later when you might get your man. Oh, I admit you're smart. You read the situation sooner than I did myself. You sensed his mood, didn't you? Something had gone wrong and you meant to do the comforting. I kept my mouth shut because it wasn't my business, but I'm making it my business now. *You* wouldn't stand for a female creeping around *your* husband would you? You'd scratch her eyes out because you're that type. But Sylvia couldn't. She went off, leaving the way clear in case he wanted it that way."

"Then they didn't go together?" Christine triumphed. "I knew it."

"No," Kate had tripped up and felt shaken.

"Then they've parted? What are you keeping me here for? Poor Jeremy. I feel so sorry for him. Where is he? I don't believe he's left the ranch at all."

"Just a minute." Kate thrust the girl back into the chair as if she were a fly. "Sure they went separately—but the minute he knew, he followed. When I told him, do you know what he did—he shaved himself, and counted his money, and went right after her to bring her back—so help me God."

Christine was furious. "You only told him because you wanted him to follow her. He's not happy. Anyone can see that."

"Sure I wanted him to go, but it was up to him, wasn't it? If he hadn't gone I'd have left my job that minute—but he's no milksop."

"I know," Christine's flaming beauty taunted her as the colour rose in her face. "He's a real man."

"That's why you wanted him—that's why you set out to get him this time. You did it deliberately, seizing on the situation. You'd like him to divorce Sylvia and marry you. Well, you failed—if you ever had a real chance. It isn't you he wants—it's his own wife. His going after her will make it sure."

"And what about my feelings—don't they count?" Christine demanded indignantly. "Jeremy has been sweet to me. I care for him, and I could make him happy. Doesn't that count?"

"Not around here," Kate told her firmly. "You'd best keep away. You'd better stay home where they breed your own type."

"I've never been so insulted in my life. Let me go." Tears of mortification rose in Christine's beautiful eyes.

"No, stay a minute. You don't know it, but I like you. I like your guts. But I don't like the way you've nearly mucked up this situation. Without you I believe they'd have got together on their own."

"From what you say they are getting together so that lets me out . . ."

"No. You still don't realize why. You think it's because I've connived and pointed the way to Jeremy. You little fool, you were never more mistaken. I couldn't have made him go after her. He knows what he wants."

"You talk like an old maid," Christine said furiously.

"Aye. I'm an old maid, and I can see that the wife always has the whiphand. That's what the youngsters don't realize. You forget that he loved *her* and married her, and neither of them will forget it in spite of you. A man expects an awful lot from a woman when he has to give up so much for her. Sylvia could have had him back any time she'd really tried."

"You seem to know a lot about it."

"It's just what happened," Kate bit off the words as she bit off the cotton in her mending. "He's gone of his own accord—but she left it so he could. Oh, he's friendly enough—but you see, you're not his wife." She was rubbing it in with a heavy hand and Christine shrank from her cruelty.

"Any man would go from a sense of duty," she protested weakly.

"No. If he'd been really keen on you don't you think he'd have taken advantage of the opportunity she gave him? I do. A married man can have an affair with a girl as nice as you—and the first time his wife needs him in any way, he goes right back to her. Men are like that." Kate paused, but only because she was short of breath. The tide of feeling was still running strong and she did not intend to finish until she had said all that was in her mind. It was seldom that she had such an audience. "There's something about separating a man and wife that's mean and nasty . . ."

"You talk as if I'd deliberately planned it." Christine was staring down at her clasped hands, her shoulders sagging.

"Hadn't you? You liked him from the first minute, but he wasn't tempted then. The second time you came you were on to it in a flash. You wouldn't have stolen her money, but you meant to steal her man."

"I'll sue you for that."

"Go ahead. Neither of us has any witnesses—thank God."

"It's too big a subject," Christine said slowly.

"What I'm condemning is where an unmarried girl goes right after a man, and takes him away from his lawful wife. Sure you knew why the rules were made? I'm pretty sure you've tried this before."

Christine flushed dully at the innuendo in the loud voice. "I hate you."

"Just remember that most married folks try to stick to the rules—if they can." Kate's voice rolled like thunder and when she stopped the quietness stirred her. Christine continued to sit, all the starch gone from her slim body. She did not appear to have strength to leave her tormentor.

"Sometimes single women do live with married men," she said finally, glancing up at Kate.

"I know—but are they ever really happy? How can they be?"

"It's all a matter of how you look at these things. It's a kind of happiness just to belong to the person you love."

"Well, the law's agin it. In the main it's for the best. When *you* get married you'll take every advantage of the law if the need arises. Surely a girl as attractive as you are can find a man of her own. Have a try." Kate's voice had softened.

Christine stood up hesitantly, as if she were afraid of Kate. "Can I go now?"

"Sure. Good-bye." Kate turned away as casually as if they had been discussing life in Tibet. Inside the door Christine hesitated, unsure of her ground, so unhappy and chastened that she was crying quietly.

"You've taken a lot for granted, Kate. Has it occurred to you that you might have made a mistake?"

"No—it hasn't."

"I hate you for this . . . but I wish you were my friend." Tears overflowed suddenly.

"I am," Kate told her boldly. "Do you think I'd have wasted my valuable time if you'd been just any little alley-cat? I'm particular who I talk to, I am."

"Oh, Kate . . ." Christine came flying back across the room to hug the big woman. "You've given me such a trouncing. I'll always remember—but he *is* attractive . . ."

Kate held her in gentle arms. "Maybe I was a bit on the hard side. Forget it."

"No, I won't—and one day I'm coming back again. I'll show Sylvia that there was nothing between Jeremy and me. There wasn't, you know. He—wasn't interested."

"I've got my pride, too," Kate wailed. "Shall I help you to pack?"

"No, I can manage, thank you. Kate— I shall be *able* to come back one day, won't I? You won't have told everyone about this, will you?"

"Not on your life," Kate promised heavily. "I'm no more proud of it than you are. I've an idea I've been a bit of a fool."

Christine laughed ruefully. "Looking at it from Jeremy's side—you have."

When Dan came in an hour later, Kate told him that he was needed to help Christine put her bags and boxes in the little roadster in which she had arrived. He cleaned the car carefully and an hour later they watched Christine drive away down the lane.

Dan came back slowly to where Kate was preparing a meal for them both. She looked upset and very cross. He looked at her speculatively. Kate was banging pans about and appeared insensible to the pandemonium she produced. She was evidently disturbed about something.

They were silent during the first part of the meal. Kate seemed preoccupied and

250

forgot to ask him to have a second helping of pie.

"Kate . . ."

"Help yourself," she spoke absently.

"It wasn't that. I was wondering . . ."

"What about? What a man you are for mumbling."

"You and me, Kate—alone on this ranch. It doesn't look so well, Kate, does it?"

"Why not?" she snapped. "I'm respectable, aren't I?"

"I wasn't suggesting anything no different . . ."

"I hope not indeed," she looked at him belligerently.

"But I was thinking that maybe now was the time to get married like . . ."

"Like what?" Kate demanded, her colour rising. She glanced away restlessly.

"Like you once promised me. What went wrong, Kate, dear?"

She sniffed. "You should know."

He hesitated before moving his chair closer to hers. His leathery face was smiling for he knew his Kate in spite of what had come between them. "If it's going to be ever it had better be now."

"I'll think about it," she promised, and for the first time her glance wavered before his. "Dan, I'm wondering if maybe I'm not the biggest fool you ever met."

"Nay, lass, you couldn't be that," Dan assured her. "How long will it take you to think about it?"

"Until the morning." Her reply was as simple as his question.

"Thank you, Kate. I'm sixty—did you know?"

"I'm a shrewd judge of age," Kate told him, but she would not tell him her own age. They both knew that she congratulated herself on being at least ten years younger. "Now get out of my kitchen; I'm going to be mighty busy clearing up after all these folks that have left us."

"I'm glad Christine has gone," Dan said mildly, his eyes on her hot face.

"So am I," Kate could not have agreed more heartily as she looked at him over her broad shoulder. "But not for the same reason you are."

That night she cooked a banquet for the two of them. "All that stuff might have gone bad. She'd bought in plenty, not knowing they'd be away."

"Their loss," Dan agreed, looking across the table. The dish of cutlets was a picture, cooked to a golden brown, with the fat melting on the fork. The vegetables were steaming under the tureen lids. Dan lifted the first one—potatoes, floury and soft. His mouth watered. The next dish held runner beans; the next one contained spinach, of so soft a texture that it might have been moss. The cooking had not spoiled its colour, and Kate had chopped it so finely that not a vestige of stem remained. Butter oozed down the sides of the little mound and it was topped off with a poached egg. Kate's eyes came to his as he lifted the lid and sat looking.

Manfully he pushed a serving spoon into the soft mound. "Ah, spinach . . ."

She watched intently as he dipped in a second time before she relaxed. She pushed the other dishes towards him hospitably, and saw that his plate was well filled. Suddenly she began to laugh, at first no more than a whimper, for she had no intention of spoiling Dan with kindness . . . but the mood overcame her until she had to put down her knife and fork.

"You don't have to eat the stuff," she told him, gasping.

"Oh, come now, Kate. It's taken you seven years to get me this far—don't go back on yourself now." Dan was manfully stuffing his mouth with spinach, determined to be done with it so that he could enjoy the rest of the meal in peace. He hiccoughed suddenly. "I'll eat it if it kills me."

Kate had a spasm of mirth that stopped the meal completely. "It won't—actually it's good for you. You need more iron in your diet." She was laughing so much she could not stop him.

Dan continued to hiccough and eat, keeping busy until the last mouthful had gone. Finally he put down his fork and grinned at her. "That proves it . . ." he told her happily. "But don't ever buy the stuff again or I'll divorce you, so I will." He hiccoughed loudly to prove it conclusively. "It shows you what I want your answer to be in the morning, Kate dear."

"Get on with your meal," she told him, but Dan was no longer afraid of her quick tongue. He rose, wiping his mouth with the back of his hand, and came round to her end of the table. He kissed her on the cheek and then smiled as if he liked her.

"Of all the goings on." The decisiveness had gone out of Kate's voice.

"We can be married come week-end," he told her, walking back to his place.

Kate was struck by his sudden stand. "Is it the spinach made you say that, Dan?"

"Aye, I expect it is, lass." He smiled at her and hiccoughed again.

"Then all I can say is that it's a pity you were too stubborn to eat the stuff years ago."

This so overcame Dan that neither of them could proceed with the meal. They chuckled all through the prolonged washing-up that followed, for their affairs amused them exceedingly.

6

THERE was no anger in Sylvia's heart to tide her over the journey back to England. Had she resented what had happened, had she been able to blame Jeremy, or been fleeing from some deep injustice, it would have been easier. Instead, she experienced a deep sadness and loneliness, knowing that what she was doing might hurt Jeremy so deeply he would be unable to forgive her. Surely he would understand that the initiative was now wholly in his hands.

She blamed no one but herself, and the curious set of circumstances that had contributed to their unhappiness.

Had she been quite certain of Jeremy's reaction she might have been able to formulate some plan, but she was left suspended, unable to see her way clearly into the future.

Far back, long before she and Jeremy met, this part of the situation had been forming. How much of their happiness had been owing to his generosity, and how much to his genuine regard for her? The questions tortured her and remained unanswered. Only one part was satisfactory—she was giving him a chance to choose. If he no longer felt a desire to uphold his marriage his chance was here. It never occurred to her that he would follow her immediately. She supposed that their affairs would be conducted by post, and she would know before final arrangements were made. Jeremy's first letter would be interesting.

A new spirit took possession of her, and it was without trepidation that she boarded a 'plane for England. A year ago she would not have considered the possibility of flying so far across an ocean, now she scarcely noticed it.

"What's come over me? I'm afraid—I must be—I always have been . . ."

There was no room for fear within her now. She was frozen, unafraid because greater, more essential issues had taken possession, and made flying the Atlantic a very unimportant part of her career. The thought brought deeper ones. Life was only of value when one was able to live it fully. One could dispense with so much, but not with happiness. Jeremy had meant something to her from their first meeting and she knew now that she had been important to him, too. Their eyes had met, gravely, and that had seemed to be all. What a lot had happened since then.

The hours of that night sped slowly, yet she was conscious that she had never lived so intensely. Her thoughts were too deep for expression. For each of them there must be certainty this time. All of the future depended on them now. Without that inner self-respect she did not wish to live.

The arrival when they touched down at Prestwick was intensely interesting to Sylvia, to whom it was a new experience. She waited her turn in the lounge, finally sending a wire to Deborah, telling her the approximate time of her arrival later in the day. Other planes were ready to leave, the loudspeakers were constantly uttering warnings. Sylvia sipped her coffee mechanically. She could not have done this trip if her passport had not been in order, she thought.

She was relieved to find that both

Deborah and Jeremy's brother Davy met her train. Their welcome was hearty and sincere. They chatted easily as they led her to where Davy's car was parked. "I'm so glad you met me—not that I have any baggage—just the one case."

"Then it's a flying visit in more ways than one?" Deborah asked.

Sylvia nodded. "I—think so." This was not the moment to unburden herself, but she felt their curiosity. "This won't make any difference to your own trip. Jeremy is looking forward to that intensely. He wants to show Davy all he can of the whole district. He's planning fishing and canoeing trips, climbing a couple of mountains, some shooting, and lots of camping, of course. It's a wonderful life. He wants to explore right up the Kootenay river— something he hasn't been able to do yet. I think you'd better go well equipped, Davy."

Davy grinned, reminding her strongly of Jeremy. The brothers were very much alike, with strong faces in spite of their fairness. Davy's hair stood on end just as Jeremy's did sometimes.

"I'm having a pair of boots specially

studded," he said. "Say, Sylvia, what's it really like in BC?"

As they entered the house and ate the meal that Deborah had prepared, she was able to tell them much that had not been gleaned from their frequent letters. Davy's curiosity was keen and she drew him word pictures. "I don't want to make you dissatisfied with your life in the Bank . . ." she ended laughingly. She stressed that they would both be welcome at the ranch, for in spite of what had happened she still had faith in the future.

After the meal she strolled along the small promenade with Davy, taking his arm for the wind was keen. Across the ocean lay Ireland, and beyond it again, Canada. Their thoughts galloped ahead as they became silent.

"If we like it on this trip I'm thinking of settling in Canada," Davy said. "Deborah says she wouldn't mind."

How one's actions influenced others, she thought. Jeremy's first trip to Canada might result in the whole family following him. Davy talked of his plans and Sylvia liked his matter-of-factness, knowing that he accepted Deborah as his true mother.

"I hope you'll both like it," she said gently. Before returning she stood with her face to the breeze that lifted to them from the water. How sweet the scent of the sea. What was Jeremy doing now?

That night she told Deborah and Davy the reason for her presence there. They listened gravely, interested, but shy that she had left Jeremy. She realized that their sympathy was all with Jeremy, and they could not understand why she had left him. Because of their attitude she was driven into making explanations she had never intended to give. They were all silent.

"I suppose you couldn't have done differently under the circumstances," Deborah said finally. "I remember the incident you mention. Jeremy was young then—young and headstrong, but it pulled him up. He and Morgan were racing about town in a reckless sort of way, and it worried me. I didn't know about the girls, but I do remember how worried Jeremy was all the time Morgan was in hospital. Being responsible for that second blow was a terrible thing. All they'd meant was to have their fling after years in the army. It didn't work out too well, did it? Morgan was worse than Jeremy I think; he never listened to advice even then."

"I wonder why you never mentioned it to me during my stay here?" Sylvia asked. "I don't think it would have hurt me as much then as it did later."

"I don't think it ever crossed my mind," Deborah acknowledged. "Or if it did I felt that Jeremy would tell you himself. He should have done so . . ."

"Why?" Davy demanded. "I don't see why. Wasn't it far better to forget the whole business? Look what happened when he did rake it up."

Sylvia could see his point of view, but it would not solve the situation.

Deborah said slowly: "It was a long time before either of them met you, so I don't really know why it ranks so high in your mind, Sylvia."

"Because it ranks high in Jeremy's, I suppose." Sylvia told them. "It was between us—something we couldn't get around from the beginning. When he told me it seemed much worse than it need have done. You see . . . that—and what happened when Morgan died—through me . . . just about finished us."

"Yet neither of you were to blame," Davy suggested.

"No, but somehow we caused Morgan's death. Which ever way you look at that it doesn't make for happiness, does it?"

"I suppose not." Deborah looked at her questioningly. "What will you do if Jeremy doesn't respond the way you hope he will? Suppose he does choose Christine? You must have grounds for thinking he might."

Sylvia whitened, and they both looked away, feeling sorry for her. "I don't seem able to get so far ahead yet. I must meet that as it comes—one day at a time. I shall feel like dying if he turns from me."

"Then you do love Jeremy?"

"Oh, yes, Davy, I do—with all my heart."

It was growing late, the fire burning low. Davy bent forward to mend it, but Deborah stopped him. "I wouldn't bother; we should be in bed. Sylvia is so tired she can hardly talk. Listen, dear—here's some advice. Why don't you visit Morgan's mother and get the business settled and out of your system? It might clear the air for you."

Sylvia shrank from the suggestion. "She was so bitter that her words were like a curse. I couldn't take any more."

"It's over a year now—she may have changed. I'll go with you if you fear her alone."

"I'm not afraid physically. I just fear being hurt again. Whichever way you look at it I acted weakly and will be for ever in the wrong. I should have sought help for Morgan's mental condition. Instead I dallied, hoping he would change. If I'd acted with more courage it might all have been saved. I know now that he was not —himself."

"Please go," Deborah insisted. "You'll never forgive yourself if you don't put the whole sorry business right while you have the chance. At least you can try. You could explain it to her—she might understand better than you think."

"I'll run you over in the car," Davy offered. "Save you a lot of time."

"Thank you, Davy. It is very kind of you both and I'm glad to accept." She felt very tired, for the previous night's sleeplessness was telling on her. After the quiet months on the ranch life was moving at a faster speed and she felt unequal to the pace.

Deborah watched her. "You're terribly tired now. I wish it could all be settled so that you could be happy again."

Sylvia turned away. "Yes. I'll go to bed now, Deborah. Thank you both for your kindness to me today . . . and for listening so patiently. I feel better already."

"We'll get away early in the morning," Davy said. "The car is ready."

Sylvia was unequal to facing the journey alone, but with Davy it would be different. Did he know that? His understanding surprised her. Possibly he was helping her because he hoped that it would finally help Jeremy's cause.

The following morning Deborah wakened her, and she dressed with care for the journey. It was almost a year since her marriage to Jeremy, and she was constantly reminded of the weeks she had spent here before joining him on the ranch. She had dressed in this very room, her hopes high, her faith unimpaired.

Today she felt nervous and unequal to facing the interview that lay ahead. Somehow it would pass. Tonight it would be over—for good or ill.

So much was at stake, all of the future, wherein might be so much for both of them.

Davy came in from the crisp air, having been to a garage for petrol.

"We filled her up. We'll not meet much traffic on the roads today."

Deborah packed sandwiches, and prepared a good breakfast before they left.

Davy was waiting when Sylvia came down in her thick travelling coat. His eyes approved her. "You look—pretty good. One of these days I'll pick me a girl."

She smiled at him, before Deborah kissed her good-bye. "Now don't forget. You have a deal of straightening out to do. Don't fall down on that. Just keep right on until things clear up the way you want them to. It can't be any worse and it may possibly be a lot better."

Sylvia wondered if there was anything left to clear up. The situation was tragically clear as it was. There seemed no real solution.

Davy was a good driver and did not take unnecessary risks. It was nearly eleven o'clock when he stopped the car at their destination. "Would you like some coffee before you go in?"

"No, thank you. You have some while you are waiting for me." They had arranged that she should meet Morgan's mother alone.

He nodded, his face serious and kind. "You're not scared, are you? She can't eat you. If you're not back here in an hour I'll come and rout you out. That do?"

"Thank you, Davy." For some reason they shook hands. "An hour should be plenty."

She walked away, feeling cold. There was nothing inspiring about the coming interview. Indeed, it was possible that Morgan's mother would refuse to see her. They had parted in such complete antagonism that it was impossible for there to be a welcome. She found the house easily, for she had visited it several times with Morgan. She hoped there would be no one at home, but when she heard the bell peal, someone came in answer.

It was Morgan's mother, and her surprise was genuine and complete.

"You—Sylvia. I'd no idea you were in England."

"I—only arrived yesterday." Sylvia hesitated but the woman invited her in with an imperative wave of her hand.

"Do come in. You must have come with a purpose. It's nice of you to look me up." She led the way into the lounge, a pleasant, homely room, an index to the character of the woman herself. Everything was clean and polished. Whatever else she was an excellent housewife. The flowered chintz curtains at the windows were attractive. "Sit down. I'm alone. Did you know that my husband died four months ago?"

"No. I'm sorry to hear that. I haven't had any news of you."

"It was a blow. I thought I couldn't bear it for a while, but one has to learn to take what comes along in life. I'm getting over it now. It never rains but it pours and Morgan's death started a rain of bad luck for me."

Sylvia glanced apprehensively at her

passive face. "I'm sorry. I know what that meant to you."

"Perhaps. You have to experience it to know the pain it can be. But you did know about Morgan—what am I saying? I get confused sometimes."

They were coming to it, and Sylvia strove to hold it at bay to give herself time. Her heart was beating suffocatingly, and she longed for air. This woman had once hurt her so deeply that she felt unable to forgive her.

She drew a quivering breath, and a shiver ran through her cold body.

"Can I make you a cup of tea? It won't take long."

"No, thank you. I haven't time." You never had time for anything you didn't want to do, she thought wildly.

"You're married again now, of course. I always liked Jeremy Lang—not that we ever saw much of Morgan's friends."

The words opened the way for Sylvia and she plunged in. "Yet you knew I could never be happy with Jeremy when —you told me I was responsible for Morgan's death. You knew that you were making life into a small hell for me, didn't you?" Sylvia's low voice rose, for she considered that this woman had not dealt fairly with her.

"You're too sensitive. A bolder person wouldn't have felt so bad," the older woman looked at her in some surprise. "Yes, I did want to hurt you, to make you feel some of the anguish I was feeling at losing my only son. Since then I'd have written to you, but didn't have your address, and other things put it from my mind."

"After Morgan died I was very ill. Then I joined Jeremy in Canada. We tried to be happy . . ."

"Are you both on holiday?" There was curiosity in the quiet voice.

"No. What you did—unsettled our marriage. I never forgot for one moment that you considered me responsible. I've left Jeremy . . ."

"Don't you get on together?"

Sylvia winced. "In a sense we get on well together, but the other factor defeated us. How can we be happy together, when we take our happiness at Morgan's expense? It's why I am here now. You must know in your heart that I was not responsible for causing Morgan's death. You must . . . you must . . . I couldn't be, only so far as we were together when it happened. It was an accident; it might have happened anywhere. It happened when he was with me. That is what is undermining my strength. I wish I could make you see. Then Jeremy told me . . . about the time when he . . . and Morgan had a fight . . . and afterwards he had to wear a plate in his head. Jeremy shrinks from that, too . . . and . . ."

"Just a minute. Aren't you mixing your facts. That isn't the way Morgan told it to me, and I was at the hospital almost daily for some weeks. What had Jeremy to do with that?" She looked at Sylvia in a puzzled way. "They were with a couple of girls. Jeremy was inclined to scrap—they were both drunk, of course. A couple of fools, but Morgan knocked *Jeremy* down . . . and one of the girls tried to get Morgan's wallet. He resisted, naturally, and he never quite knew what happened, but when he came to both their wallets were missing and he was in hospital . . ."

Sylvia felt as if the world was slowing down with terrible emphasis. The buzzing in her ears grew to deafening proportions. "I don't understand. Morgan . . . that is, Jeremy thinks he's responsible for what happened to Morgan . . ."

"No. I don't think so, Sylvia. If Morgan allowed him to think that then it was devilment. You know what Morgan was—I don't deny his sense of humour was strange . . ."

"Jeremy certainly said that Morgan never seemed to bear him any ill will."

"Why should he?" The older woman looked grey and worn. "I don't know what you are thinking, but Jeremy never had anything to do with that. Morgan laughed when he told us—laughed because a slip of a girl managed to knock him out when Jeremy couldn't do it himself. He never sought to hide the facts."

"Oh," Sylvia spoke on a spent breath. "Can I tell Jeremy? We've both felt like murderers, for between us it seemed that we accounted for Morgan's death. It's come between us, spoiling our happiness. I wonder if he'll be able to believe? He'll be so glad."

"He'll believe—because he'll want to believe."

"I was going to leave Morgan weeks before he died. If only I had . . . but I tried to make our marriage a success."

"Yes, Morgan had faults. You had plenty to take; I realize that now."

"I know he realized that I was going to leave him. I'd done my utmost—until one night he said: 'I'll kill you before I'll let you walk out on me. My woman isn't going to leave me.' It was from that threat I was flying—when the accident happened. Now do you see? Your words sealed his in my mind in a terrible, final agony of doubt."

"Our last meeting was—hideous," the old woman admitted slowly. "Have you left Jeremy—for good?"

"I don't know. I long to be rid of that memory. The future must come right or I can never live with Jeremy again. What you have told me will help—he'll be grateful."

"Is he jealous of Morgan—of your previous marriage?"

"Yes, yet he is too generous a man to . . . to . . . but he can't bear it when I dwell on the past. He resents so much—can't you find something to comfort me also? I need help so desperately." Sylvia spoke miserably.

There was a short silence broken only by the old woman's stormy breathing. "I blame you for not casting off this feeling long ago. You were ill so I suppose my words took root in your mind. Will you try to believe that it was my own disappointment and anger that spoke that day? I knew all these things, but would not admit them even to myself. I wanted my son back—not only physically—but spiritually too. I longed to be able to revere his memory, but I had knowledge of all that you were enduring at his hands. Do you suppose that I was blind to his true nature? Didn't I know that he drank heavily and that you could scarcely bear to live with him any longer? I wanted to think that it was because you didn't love him that he was dissatisfied, but there was so much more to it than that. How could you love him when he deliberately tried to hurt you? You have not tried to forgive him in death, as we all must, as I have been able to do. You must if you mean to find happiness, I think. Morgan is only as strong as your mind allows him to be—I have realized that, and you must also. I was bitter, too, for a while. I had to blame someone; you were close—and vulnerable. I tried to think that you had caused the accident in some way, but I knew you hadn't. How can I change your conception of what happened? You were always too gentle for Morgan. Your breeding appealed to him, for in those early days he was particular. I say this without any bitterness left in me. The hard streak in his nature was to be regretted, may I be forgiven for saying so much. No, you didn't cause his death, Sylvia. Most of what happened in his life was his own fault —in later years anyway."

Sylvia could not find an answer. She listened with her whole being. The quiet words were sinking in like rain on parched earth, sinking deep, healing tortured roots. Their good could not be estimated.

"I was wrong to talk to you the way I did that night. My own pain was responsible."

Sylvia wanted the quiet voice to go for ever, to continue talking so that what had been crooked in her mind might become straight again. She was so mentally jaded that she could not think ahead any longer. There was only this unemotional pitiful voice telling her these truths.

"Can't you manage to patch up your marriage with Jeremy? It's such a pity to add that to the other failures around Morgan's life. Don't let him reach out from the past to destroy—as he destroyed in life. Try to live hopefully."

"I can't thank you enough," Sylvia's voice trembled. "You have—released me . . ."

"It was in your own mind that the curse lay, because you had not learned tolerance. Peace might have come had you thought to forgive *me*."

The idea that she had been at fault in not forgiving the bitter words, was a new one, and Sylvia pondered it for a while.

"Will you return to Canada?"

"I don't know just what will happen." Sylvia flushed warmly, then her pallor returned, showing how her features had sharpened during the past weeks. "He may not want me back. A man doesn't enjoy seeing his wife walk out—as I have done."

"Put your pride in your pocket and go

back to him. We make too much of our pride. A man can understand love and kindness when it's offered sincerely—by the woman he loves. A wife can always find a way."

"Unless there is someone else . . ."

"*Even* if there is someone else. Marriages are not made in a day." The correction was strange, coming from such a source.

Sylvia looked at her in surprise. "It's all such a—surprise . . ."

"Yes. It must be, but if I've spoiled your happiness I must try to repair the damage. I used to think of you as an inhuman young person without feelings. That was one of my mistakes. I wish you'd forgive me, Sylvia."

The apology did not come easily and Sylvia doubted her hearing for a moment. She looked quickly into the eyes so like Morgan's and read the appeal in them. Gently she took the old woman's hands into hers. She carried them to her face as she answered in a slow, moved voice. "I do forgive—so willingly. Let's not even remember. We both had so much to forgive. If you feel that you hurt me that day, this more than makes it good. This is a new lease of life for us. You are generous." They sat down on the settee close together. "I've always respected you, for you were Morgan's mother. Some day —when you get over this, will you come to Canada to pay us a visit? Would you like to do that?"

"Yes, I'll come. It wouldn't hurt either of you now, would it? I'd love to see you happy again as you were when I first knew you."

"I'll be happy again," Sylvia promised.

A loud ring on the doorbell startled them both. The older woman went to answer the ring, while Sylvia straightened her dark hair. Davy had come in search of her as he had promised, and she smiled at him as he stood framed in the doorway.

"I thought you'd got lost, so I came to get you," Davy muttered.

"Please stay and have a meal with me. I can't let you go like this." Morgan's mother stood between them. "You're very like Jeremy, aren't you? For a minute I thought you were he at the door."

"I'm an inch shorter," Davy admitted.

"You'll stay?" she insisted. "You both look to need a square meal."

"We'd love to stay. Let us help you." Sylvia felt the strangeness as they followed her into the kitchen. Davy opened a tin of tomato soup. His presence brought back a sense of reality, and soon their tongues were loosened. Davy was puzzled, for there was such an air of relief about the two women. But he joined in and decided to await the explanations.

"She flew over," Davy said, as they ate the excellent meal later. "Maybe she'll let you touch her for luck. I envy you that air trip, Sylvia."

"I didn't think much about it; my mind was on more important matters."

"Will you fly back?" Morgan's mother asked curiously.

"No, I'd be too scared." She laughed ruefully, for it was the truth; she was herself again.

They left the house a couple of hours later. As quickly as possible Sylvia told Davy what had occurred, and then they both dropped silent, each busy with their own thoughts. when they drew close to their destination Davy said: "Are you returning to Canada as soon as you can book a passage?"

"Yes—this changes so much. We can find our way now. Oh, Davy, when you marry let it be straightforward and ordinary. It's so hard to bear when it isn't."

"It will be ordinary enough," Davy grinned at her and she was reminded of Jeremy again. "On my salary there won't be much chance of anything else."

Sylvia felt cheered. The salty air with its cooling tang welcomed them long before they saw it. As they drew on to the little promenade in front of the open gate she turned to Davy and thanked him warmly.

"You're a wonderful brother-in-law, Davy. I'll try to do something nice for you one day to make up." She got out of the car. "That was a long drive . . ."

The front door was thrown open and sharp steps rang on the path.

"Oh . . . Jeremy . . . Jeremy . . ." she whispered faintly.

Jeremy seemed to assess the situation quickly, primed no doubt by Deborah. "Where on earth have you two been all day?"

Her colour was fluctuating and she

wished she did not feel so nervous. Her heart was singing a paean of thanksgiving and praise. He had come. All the way from Canada he had come.

Davy shook hands with him, laughing delightedly, slapping his shoulder with his free hand. "You son of a gun . . ."

"Come inside." Jeremy was the more self-possessed of the three, but he had been awaiting them and it could not be a surprise to him as it was to them.

Sylvia walked quickly up the path to the house. A bird was singing in the trees at the foot of the garden and she had never heard a sweeter song.

Jeremy had come.

7

THEY stood about undecidedly. There had been no real greeting yet for Sylvia, but she was so caught up in the excitement of Jeremy's arrival that she had no quarrel with that. He must have cared, to come so quickly and so far. There was a grimness about his face, not reflected on those of his stepmother and brother.

Sylvia waited, still in her outdoor coat, for the evening was cold.

"I expect you two have plenty to discuss," Deborah said, while Davy was running the car into the garage. "Wasn't it a complete surprise, Sylvia? I was amazed when Jeremy walked in. Will you have something to eat? I'm trying to get a meal together."

Sylvia had no appetite and she felt too apprehensive to be able to sit at a table talking generally. "I don't want anything, but Jeremy may."

"No. Deborah gave me an excellent

snack less than an hour ago." Jeremy's voice held no cordiality and he stood obviously waiting for something.

"Why not go in the lounge and have a nice talk?" Deborah coaxed, trying to help things along. "The fire is lit in there."

"That's an idea." Jeremy held the door open for Sylvia to pass him into the lounge. Her hands were deep in her coat pockets but feeling her own tension as a barrier, she took off the coat and laid it over the back of a chair. She was overwhelmed by his presence, but his mood was strange, antagonistic too, and she would be thankful when they understood one another again. She shivered suddenly and went nearer to the fire.

"Jeremy—you came . . ." she began hesitantly, knowing that one of them had to break through the barrier of silence. "I'm so glad."

"What did you expect me to do?" he demanded dryly. He took out his pipe. "Mind if I smoke?"

"No. You know I never mind. I didn't expect you to come, Jeremy. I—hoped you would write perhaps."

He lighted the pipe thoughtfully. "After

all, we are man and wife— a point you seem to have overlooked lately. What else could I do except take you back where you belong? Anything odd about that?"

"No. No . . . not really." If only he would give some sign of relenting, she thought miserably. Obviously he had not come in a forgiving mood after all. "I'm glad you came."

"Weren't you a bit hasty—coming away like this?"

"I had to come—I had to be certain that you wanted me at the ranch . . ."

He looked across at her sharply. "Did you honestly doubt that?"

"Yes." She could not meet the look in his keen eyes.

"You amaze me. We must have failed each other badly somewhere if you truly doubted that." He was silent, drawing on the pipe contemplatively. "I supose I've got the rest of it correct—you wanted to give me a chance to bring you back if I felt that way?"

She nodded, not trusting herself to speak.

"Complimentary to me, aren't you?" he said grimly. "What do you think I am?

We seem to have worked ourselves into a nice spot, don't we?"

"Perhaps it's finished now," she suggested hopefully.

"I hope so. For my sake as well as yours. I'm sick of all the doubts. We can't go on like this; we have to remember that we're settling down. The Lord knows how we intend to achieve that point. You can't fly over here every time we quarrel."

"Was it—only that?" she spoke in a whisper.

He looked at her sharply, seeing her not as his wife, but as a woman in need of help. "Why don't you sit down? You look tired. I'm not a gaoler."

She sat down in the chair he drew forward for her, glad to rest. "It—should all be much easier now—for both of us."

"In what way? Don't you want to return with me?" He was struck by something in her attitude, and watched her through narrowed lids. In spite of her apprehension she was composed and thoughtful.

"Yes, I want to go back with you, Jeremy."

"Well, then . . . why are we as awry as any couple I've ever known?"

She shook her head. "I'm glad you've come anyway. Deborah asked me last night what I would do if you didn't want me back, and I couldn't answer then. I knew how terrified I would be if I'd destroyed your love for me."

He made an impatient gesture. "For goodness sake don't talk rubbish. Love is not quite the ephemeral thing you seem to think. Listen—there are faults on both sides. I'm not going to take the whole blame—it was about equal, I'd say."

She smiled and nodded. "Why don't *you* sit down, too? You sound angry."

"I didn't realize I was holding forth like a schoolmaster," he said stiffly. "A bad-tempered one at that, eh?"

She realized that he was trying to make it easier for them both. Her action had shocked him but he appeared relieved that he was not facing active opposition. The thought brought a wan smile to her white face. He sat down in what had been his father's armchair, facing her.

"Did Deborah tell you that Davy took me to meet Morgan's mother today?" she asked.

"Yes—and I'd have thought you'd have

kept your distance from that woman. I can't begin to understand your motives, Sylvia. Deborah didn't comment but I was fighting mad for awhile. What's behind it —I'd like to know?"

She saw his increasing irritation and knew that he had deliberately kept his stepmother from telling him what she knew. "I went because Deborah advised it —and also because I felt she might be able to help me to get away from the misery of our previous meeting. I feel happier now. In fact—free again. I've laid my ghosts, Jeremy—and yours, too . . ." she added slowly.

He glanced at her again. "What do you mean by that?"

"She told me . . . when I had explained the way things were between you and me, that you were never responsible for Morgan's condition . . ." She glanced into his face seeing his sudden tension and dismay. "She was with him daily while he was in hospital and he spoke quite openly about that—said it was one of the girls who tried to steal his wallet. He resisted her, and she pushed him so that he fell and just blacked out. She did get his wallet —yours too, I think?"

"But Morgan said . . . and I knew . . ." He shaded his face with one hand, the pipe forgotten.

"If Morgan let you think otherwise, she said it would just be his strange idea of a joke. He—knocked you out first, he told her so, and you were both found . . ." she looked at him with tightening lips. "It's pretty disgusting whichever way you look at it, Jeremy. Those girls absconded with your money, and serve you right, too. Of course you were young then but that doesn't excuse you."

The severity of her summing up brought a smile to his face. "Just a minute—let's straighten out as we go. You're quite sure about this?"

"Quite sure. She was amazed that it had ever troubled you. When she realized how we had felt hounded by the double misfortune she tried to put it right—for both of us. I felt you would be so grateful for that. You could confirm it any time. She would probably be glad to see you, for she asked about you almost at once, as if she liked you. To her you are Morgan's friend, not his enemy."

"We were dead drunk at the time," he admitted grudgingly. "I never did remember much about the real facts. Morgan let me think . . ." The colour drained out of his tanned face. "Anyhow . . . forget it. She wasn't quite the witch you'd been thinking either? What else did she say?"

"She—proved to be an unexpected friend. She absolved me completely. She doesn't blame me, and she said I might have found release long ago had I felt able to forgive her for what she said. I'm grateful to her beyond expression." She rapidly reviewed what had been said during the interview, knowing that he wished to hear.

"Then it was worth a visit?" His smile was more friendly, his gaze lingered on her thoughtfully. "I think I get the idea. How strange. You should have made this visit months ago, Sylvia—before we got estranged. . . eh?"

Sylvia moved and knelt on the rug at Jeremy's knees. She took his right hand in hers gently and held it, looking up at him pleadingly. "I beg your pardon, Jeremy. Please forgive what I have done in my misery. I doubted even your love, because something held me in the past. I know now what it was and I'm released. I meant to return to you to ask forgiveness—but you came instead. Can you forgive me?"

Her voice had never held a lovelier note, a more tender cadence. "She told me to go back to you, Jeremy. To show my love . . . she said any man would understand and forgive if the woman he loved and wanted asked him . . ."

He put both arms around her and drew her close. "If there was ever anything to forgive you, darling, I forgave it long ago. I've been a boor to hold out against you so long. You wanted to be friends weeks ago, didn't you, but I wouldn't . . . I wanted you to suffer a bit too. What a fool I've been. Let's try to forget it all now, shall we?"

"I can if you can," she told him.

He leaned back, drawing her with him. His pipe lay unnoticed on the table near them. Christine's name had not come into the conversation, and Sylvia realized how foolish she had been to think that his interest might ever lie in that direction. Her actions might have pushed him towards Christine. She knew now that Jeremy had not once thought of her in any but a friendly way. Whatever had been in the past Jeremy had come to his man's estate, and his marriage stood between him and any light emotion. She was quietly glad as she rested against his shoulder.

"I love you, Sylvia. You've got to believe that. We've shared a lot of things —happiness and misery. I hope we're through it and I can certainly do something as easy as forgetting. We'll never speak of any of this again." He drew her closer. "You feel the same way, don't you, darling?" His voice was assured. "You still like me?"

"Naturally." She began to smile against him. She drew back as she broke into delighted laughter. He held her firmly so that he could see her face.

"What's the joke?"

"It isn't a joke. I'm just terribly happy. I'm just thankful that you feel this way because . . . it might be awkward if you didn't . . . considering . . ."

"Considering what?" Her hesitation

focussed his attention on her again, and he began to smile, too. "Anything I should know?"

"Yes. We're both going to get to know someone rather well in less than six months' time. How will you like to be a father, Jeremy?"

He drew her back to him quickly. "You know how I feel about that. When did you know?"

"A few weeks ago. I was panic-stricken for a while and didn't know what to do. Your attitude to me kept me silent. I'm sorry now." She rubbed her face against his collar, mutely asking forgiveness. "I wanted to tell you so often but couldn't when you looked so cross. And I knew you'd guess soon anyway."

"Are you glad—about the baby?" he demanded.

"Yes—are you?"

"I'm delighted. I wish I'd known before. What a heel I've been."

"It's why I had to be sure about the way you felt—if you really wanted me back. I didn't want you putting up with me out of a sense of duty. I wanted you to come without knowing. Oh, I've just been muddling through in my usual way . . ."

They both smiled. "Then I acted in a most correct manner? Oh, darling, this is going to mean so much to us. Ever since Janet and Gabriel were at the ranch last summer I've hoped we'd have youngsters, too."

"Oh, ours will be much superior," she promised, laughing happily. "Jeremy, in spite of everything I've been careful, for I wanted this baby as much as you do."

"We'll get back to the ranch as soon as we can. Anyone else know?"

"Not anyone."

"Now I know why we couldn't make up our minds about that lower room. It will be excellent as a nursery. I'll get to work on it when we get back."

They talked on until Deborah came to the door. "I hadn't heard either a bullet or a scream, so concluded it might be safe to come," she informed them cheerfully. "Here's some tea. You must be needing it." She pushed the trolley before her with determination and began to dispense the tea. Davy followed her with a plate of sandwiches.

Nearly two weeks later they arrived back at the ranch. Dusk was laying gentle fingers on the landscape as they honked their way up the lane in a borrowed car.

"I'll widen this one day," Jeremy promised.

Dan came to open the gate, with Bing barking at his heels. Their noisy welcome caused lights to spring up in at least three cabins. Dan shook hands as if he were glad to see them again. His leathery countenance was split in two with his smiles.

"Those lights? Have we guests?" Sylvia asked. The question was answered when she heard flying feet coming across the clearing. Janet's three sons raced towards her, clad in pyjamas with thick dressing gowns over them. They rushed at Jeremy and danced round him.

"It's a surprise," Tony yelled at the top of his treble voice.

"Mother said we could—whenever you came—so we're here . . ." Charles spoke more composedly, but he was excited, too.

"We've had whooping cough—Charles

brought it home from school." Pat spoke as if Charles had done something of considerable merit.

"That's why we are here so much earlier than intended," Janet joined the excited group. "They're quite over it now but they can recuperate here more quickly than anywhere else. How are you, Sylvia, Jeremy?"

No one appeared capable of answering a sensible question, but the goodwill was in evidence as they surged towards the cabins. Gabriel strolled to meet them, smiling broadly. In a most delightful way it was taken for granted that they would all hear an exact account of what had happened on the trip. Sylvia's eyes shone as she ushered the little boys ahead of her.

"Where's Kate?" Sylvia spoke to Dan who was helping Jeremy with the baggage.

"She's waiting like . . ." Dan grunted over his shoulder, and she felt startled when she realized that he had actually winked at her.

Kate came to the door, filling it in her bulky fashion.

She embraced Sylvia and kissed her soundly. "I'm glad you are back, my child, but I must tell you right away . . ." she warned in an awful voice. "Dan and I were married two weeks ago come Saturday."

"So that's what happens the minute my back is turned," Jeremy said.

"I'm delighted to hear it," Sylvia told her warmly. "I thought you might."

Kate was surprised. "Did you?"

"Knowing you two . . ."

Kate grinned, her brown face flushing. She changed the subject firmly. "I told Jeremy your address—he made me."

"I think we'd better drop that subject, don't you, Kate?"

"Aye. Happen it might be as well."

Sylvia went into the cabin. The long table was spread for a banquet. The children were evidently in the secret for they were already finding their places. Kate had cooked a meal fit for a king and knew it, too. She beamed as they all did justice to her artistry. Four chickens were done to a turn. The sweet was guaranteed not to give nightmares. Roasted apples were oozing with butter and sugar which melted down the sides in luscious cascades of goodness. Each had a cherry which served as a head.

Chopped almonds made chubby arms. The apples melted like snow as the spoons were pushed into them.

Jeremy sighed reminiscently. "Home again. Now I know it's true."

Kate flushed warmly, and smiled down the length of the table. Her eyes were kind as she saw the three little boys industriously mopping up every morsel of the fruit. "You know, I always thought I didn't like children—but I do."

"Of course you do. Kate, you're a woman in a thousand."

"Aye, she is that," Dan agreed unexpectedly.

Jeremy brought a small case to the table. "Lucky for you you remembered the children," he said to Sylvia. There were toys for each of the boys, delightful, unusual toys which they had not seen before. A scarf for Dan, headshawl for Kate, gloves for Janet, tobacco for Gabriel. Sylvia dispensed the gifts briskly. Paper and string strewed the table. The clamour of talk was deafening. Kate got up finally to clear the dishes away.

"Now children, off to bed," Janet spoke authoritatively. "I only promised that you could stay up late—not all night. It's all over now until morning."

"You *will* tell us about the aeroplane again in the morning?" Charles insisted. "I like aeroplanes, you know."

Sylvia promised, slipping back into the old routine that she had never thought to know again. It was as if the weeks of unhappiness had never been. Jeremy met her when she was returning to their cabin. The silence was settling over the ranch for the night. She remembered that silence and knew she had looked forward to the peace it brought.

Jeremy fell into step with her. "Tired, darling?" There was a tender note in his deep voice.

"Yes, but not too tired for a walk. Let's go down on the beach, Jeremy."

The air was soft and cold. Arm in arm they set out for their walk, remembering the first time they had trodden this path together.

"That was a lovely welcome," she said. "They tried to show us, didn't they?"

He nodded, smoking contentedly. They paced the beach, keeping in the silvery path of the moon, whose light caught every wave tip, silvering the outline of the great trees, bringing to enchanting life the sombre mountains.

"Exquisite." These months would ever remain in her memory, she thought. Life was slowing down for her, the tempo becoming even and pleasant, and she gave herself joyfully to this period of waiting that was hers. Jeremy smiled down at her as they stood looking out across the silvered landscape.

"Let's get back home," he said, his voice deep against the stillness.

They turned, seeing the still lighted cabins, as if the occupants found it difficult to settle after the excitement of the evening. In spite of his delicacy Gabriel's was the strength that held his little family together, Sylvia thought. Without him Janet might fall by the wayside. How strange was the dependence of all human beings on others, yet how essentially alone against the great realities.

Jeremy put his arm about her waist as they stood looking, remembering, hoping. A shadow crossed the face of the moon, touching them lightly for a brief moment. When it had passed they smiled at each other. The night was even brighter than it had been. The moment held a poignancy of meaning they could scarcely bear.

"Home . . ." Jeremy said.

THE END

We hope this Large Print edition gives you the pleasure and enjoyment we ourselves experienced in its publication.

There are now more than 2,000 titles available in this ULVERSCROFT Large print Series. Ask to see a Selection at your nearest library.

The Publisher will be delighted to send you, free of charge, upon request a complete and up-to-date list of all titles available.

Ulverscroft Large Print Books Ltd.
The Green, Bradgate Road
Anstey
Leicestershire
LE7 7FU
England

GUIDE
TO THE COLOUR CODING
OF
ULVERSCROFT BOOKS

Many of our readers have written to us expressing their appreciation for the way in which our colour coding has assisted them in selecting the Ulverscroft books of their choice. To remind everyone of our colour coding—this is as follows:

BLACK COVERS
Mysteries

★

BLUE COVERS
Romances

★

RED COVERS
Adventure Suspense and General Fiction

★

ORANGE COVERS
Westerns

★

GREEN COVERS
Non-Fiction

ROMANCE TITLES
in the
Ulverscroft Large Print Series

The Smile of the Stranger	*Joan Aiken*
Busman's Holiday	*Lucilla Andrews*
Flowers From the Doctor	*Lucilla Andrews*
Nurse Errant	*Lucilla Andrews*
Silent Song	*Lucilla Andrews*
Merlin's Keep	*Madeleine Brent*
Tregaron's Daughter	*Madeleine Brent*
The Bend in the River	*Iris Bromige*
A Haunted Landscape	*Iris Bromige*
Laurian Vale	*Iris Bromige*
A Magic Place	*Iris Bromige*
The Quiet Hills	*Iris Bromige*
Rosevean	*Iris Bromige*
The Young Romantic	*Iris Bromige*
Lament for a Lost Lover	*Philippa Carr*
The Lion Triumphant	*Philippa Carr*
The Miracle at St. Bruno's	*Philippa Carr*
The Witch From the Sea	*Philippa Carr*
Isle of Pomegranates	*Iris Danbury*
For I Have Lived Today	*Alice Dwyer-Joyce*
The Gingerbread House	*Alice Dwyer-Joyce*
The Strolling Players	*Alice Dwyer-Joyce*
Afternoon for Lizards	*Dorothy Eden*
The Marriage Chest	*Dorothy Eden*

Samantha	*Dorothy Eden*
Waiting for Willa	*Dorothy Eden*
Winterwood	*Dorothy Eden*
Countess	*Josephine Edgar*
The Emerald Peacock	*Katharine Gordon*
Jane of Gowlands	*Anne Hepple*
Rebel Heiress	*Jane Aiken Hodge*
On The Night of the Seventh Moon	
	Victoria Holt
Wind on the Heath	*Naomi Jacob*
It Was The Lark	*Catherine MacArthur*
The Empty House	*Rosamunde Pilcher*
Sleeping Tiger	*Rosamunde Pilcher*
Under Gemini	*Rosamunde Pilcher*
Wychwood	*Nicole St. John*
The Reluctant Orphan	*Sara Seale*
To Catch a Unicorn	*Sara Seale*
The Truant Bride	*Sara Seale*
The Blue Sapphire	*D. E. Stevenson*
Five Windows	*D. E. Stevenson*
Kate Hardy	*D. E. Stevenson*
Sarah Morris Remembers	*D. E. Stevenson*
Sarah's Cottage	*D. E. Stevenson*
Summerhills	*D. E. Stevenson*
Adair of Starlight Peaks	*Essie Summers*
The Forbidden Valley	*Essie Summers*
Moon Over the Alps	*Essie Summers*
Not by Appointment	*Essie Summers*

South Island Stowaway	*Essie Summers*
The Painted Caves	*Kate Thompson*
Richard's Way	*Kate Thompson*
The Silver Nightingale	*Sylvia Thorpe*
A Visit to Marchmont	*Frances Turk*
The Hospital in Buwambo	*Anne Vinton*
The Gone-Away Man	*Lucy Walker*
Heaven is Here	*Lucy Walker*
Home at Sundown	*Lucy Walker*
More Than All	*Marjorie Warby*
The Singing of the Nightingale	
	Marjorie Warby
All I Ask	*Anne Weale*
Hope For Tomorrow	*Anne Weale*
The Sea Waif	*Anne Weale*
Sullivan's Reef	*Anne Weale*
Seven Tears For Apollo	*Phyllis A. Whitney*
Silverhill	*Phyllis A. Whitney*
The Trembling Hills	*Phyllis A. Whitney*

THE SHADOWS
OF THE CROWN TITLES
in the
Ulverscroft Large Print Series

The Tudor Rose   *Margaret Campbell Barnes*
Brief Gaudy Hour *Margaret Campbell Barnes*
Mistress Jane Seymour   *Frances B. Clark*
My Lady of Cleves
                 Margaret Campbell Barnes
Katheryn The Wanton Queen
                            Maureen Peters
The Sixth Wife   *Jean Plaidy*
The Last Tudor King   *Hester Chapman*
Young Bess   *Margaret Irwin*
Lady Jane Grey   *Hester Chapman*
Elizabeth, Captive Princess   *Margaret Irwin*
Elizabeth and The Prince of Spain
                            Margaret Irwin
Gay Lord Robert   *Jean Plaidy*
Here Was A Man   *Norah Lofts*
Mary Queen of Scotland:
The Triumphant Year   *Jean Plaidy*
The Captive Queen of Scots *Jean Plaidy*
The Murder in the Tower   *Jean Plaidy*
The Young and Lonely King   *Jane Lane*
King's Adversary   *Monica Beardsworth*
A Call of Trumpets   *Jane Lane*

The Trial of Charles I   C. V. Wedgwood
Royal Flush   Margaret Irwin
The Sceptre and the Rose   Doris Leslie
Mary II: Queen of England   Hester Chapman
That Enchantress   Doris Leslie
The Princess of Celle   Jean Plaidy
Caroline the Queen   Jean Plaidy
The Third George   Jean Plaidy
The Great Corinthian   Doris Leslie
Victoria in the Wings   Jean Plaidy
The Captive of Kensington Palace
                                Jean Plaidy
The Queen and Lord 'M'   Jean Plaidy
The Queen's Husband   Jean Plaidy
The Widow of Windsor   Jean Plaidy
Bertie and Alix   Graham and Heather Fisher
The Duke of Windsor   Ursula Bloom

FICTION TITLES
in the
Ulverscroft Large Print Series

The Onedin Line: The High Seas
Cyril Abraham
The Onedin Line: The Iron Ships
Cyril Abraham
The Onedin Line: The Shipmaster
Cyril Abraham
The Onedin Line: The Trade Winds
Cyril Abraham

The Enemy	*Desmond Bagley*
Flyaway	*Desmond Bagley*
The Master Idol	*Anthony Burton*
The Navigators	*Anthony Burton*
A Place to Stand	*Anthony Burton*
The Doomsday Carrier	*Victor Canning*
The Cinder Path	*Catherine Cookson*
The Girl	*Catherine Cookson*
The Invisible Cord	*Catherine Cookson*
Life and Mary Ann	*Catherine Cookson*
Maggie Rowan	*Catherine Cookson*
Marriage and Mary Ann	*Catherine Cookson*
Mary Ann's Angels	*Catherine Cookson*
All Over the Town	*R. F. Delderfield*
Jamaica Inn	*Daphne du Maurier*
My Cousin Rachel	*Daphne du Maurier*

Enquiry	*Dick Francis*
Flying Finish	*Dick Francis*
Forfeit	*Dick Francis*
High Stakes	*Dick Francis*
In The Frame	*Dick Francis*
Knock Down	*Dick Francis*
Risk	*Dick Francis*
Band of Brothers	*Ernest K. Gann*
Twilight For The Gods	*Ernest K. Gann*
Army of Shadows	*John Harris*
The Claws of Mercy	*John Harris*
Getaway	*John Harris*
Winter Quarry	*Paul Henissart*
East of Desolation	*Jack Higgins*
In the Hour Before Midnight	*Jack Higgins*
Night Judgement at Sinos	*Jack Higgins*
Wrath of the Lion	*Jack Higgins*
Air Bridge	*Hammond Innes*
A Cleft of Stars	*Geoffrey Jenkins*
A Grue of Ice	*Geoffrey Jenkins*
Beloved Exiles	*Agnes Newton Keith*
Passport to Peril	*James Leasor*
Goodbye California	*Alistair MacLean*
South By Java Head	*Alistair MacLean*
All Other Perils	*Robert MacLeod*
Dragonship	*Robert MacLeod*
A Killing in Malta.	*Robert MacLeod*
A Property in Cyprus	*Robert MacLeod*

By Command of the Viceroy *Duncan MacNeil*

The Deceivers *John Masters*

Nightrunners of Bengal *John Masters*

Emily of New Moon *L. M. Montgomery*

The '44 Vintage *Anthony Price*

High Water *Douglas Reeman*

Rendezvous-South Atlantic *Douglas Reeman*

Summer Lightning *Judith Richards*

Louise *Sarah Shears*

Louise's Daughters *Sarah Shears*

Louise's Inheritance *Sarah Shears*

Beyond the Black Stump *Nevil Shute*

The Healer *Frank G. Slaughter*

Sword and Scalpel *Frank G. Slaughter*

Tomorrow's Miracle *Frank G. Slaughter*

The Burden *Mary Westmacott*

A Daughter's a Daughter *Mary Westmacott*

Giant's Bread *Mary Westmacott*

The Rose and the Yew Tree *Mary Westmacott*

Every Man a King *Anne Worboys*

The Serpent and the Staff *Frank Yerby*

FH 06-01
7/13/22 JR